Enduring Passion

Further New Contributions to
the Solution of Sex Difficulties
being the continuation of
Married Love

BY

Marie Carmichael Stopes

Doctor of Science, London ; Doctor of Philosophy, Munich;
Fellow of University College, London ; Fellow of the Royal
Society of Literature, and of the Linnean and Geological
Societies, London

SIXTH EDITION
INCLUDING ALL PRESCRIPTIONS

PUTNAM & CO., LTD.
42, GREAT RUSSELL STREET
LONDON

First published	.	October 18, 1928
Reprinted once		
Second Edition	. .	February 1929
Reprinted	. . .	August 1929
Reprinted	. .	September 1929
Third Edition	.	September 1930
Fourth Edition	. .	May 1931
Reprinted	. .	September 1932
Fifth Edition	. . .	April 1934
Reprinted . .	.	November 1934
Reprinted . .	.	July 1935
Sixth Edition	. .	August 1936
Reprinted	. . .	May 1937
Reprinted	. . .	April 1938
Reprinted	. . .	April 1938
Reprinted	. .	January 1939
Reprinted	. .	October 1939
Reprinted	. . .	July 1940
Reprinted	. .	September 1941
Reprinted	. .	October 1942
Reprinted	. .	April 1944
Reprinted	. .	August 1945
Reprinted	. .	October 1946

TRANSLATIONS

Dutch	Danish	German
Norwegian	Finnish	Spanish
	Swedish	

*Dedicated to all who are, might
be, or should be, married lovers*

Contents

Contents

Author's Preface to the Sixth Edition

MANY young people tell me they find the advice in this book a necessary complement to *Married Love*, and of use even in the earliest days of marriage. Schools have much to answer for. Some day my rage against them will reach boiling point. Meanwhile I hope this book will be of help to many married lovers.

M. C. S.

1936

Author's Preface to the Fourth Edition

SOME new matter has been added to this book.

The many readers of *Married Love*, though they may remain young in heart, cannot help Time making them grow older, and this book is for them. They live all over the world, and I send it to them with my best wishes.

M. C. S.

HINDHEAD,
   May 1931.

Author's Preface

FOR young husbands and all those betrothed in love I published my book *Married Love* ten years ago. It was designed to tell people the things *every* betrothed couple and young married pair should know. Countless expressions of gratitude from every class show it met, in some degree at any rate, a widespread need. It has been imitated very widely, its ideas absorbed, and its phraseology become part of the national vocabulary. Within a year of publishing it I was made to feel that the later phases of marriage required a comparable handling.

Youth passes, and even for married lovers problems arise, often due to bodily ailments. Many have asked me for a book on the later years. In particular those who had been married already for some years before *Married Love* appeared, and who found grooves established in wrong directions which they wished to rectify, but knew not how. Only knowledge can alter and set things right.

The first spontaneous rush of ecstatic delight in the new intimacy, of gallant optimism untouched by any experienced defeat, are so often confronted by solid obstacles to individual happiness, outlines of which rise cold and grey, no longer tinged by the roseate tints of dawn.

Then more knowledge is needed. Here it is—or at least what measure of it I can now contribute to the common fund of available help afforded by science to life.

This book, like *Married Love*, and unlike so many "sex" books, hardly touches on abnormalities, but in this later volume I try to help to remove some minor aberrations from the ideal state of perfect health. Problems which arise frequently must be faced frankly.

There is also, and that I hope may prove the book's most useful feature, a new—I believe an absolutely unrecorded—contribution to the sex problem of the ages. This is in Chapter VIII, in the form of explicit though very simple details about the actual mode and progress of the later phases of union which are calculated to enhance the quality and the permanence of love in marriage, and to defeat that tendency to exhaustion and boredom which are proverbially supposed to overtake those united in wedlock.

I am convinced that the more *happy*, child-bearing and *enduringly* passionate marriages there are in a State, the more firmly established is that State.

This book I offer to individuals with my love and sympathy, and in the hope that it may add to their lasting happiness: to the State I offer it because, if it should raise the standard of married happiness, it will be a greater national bulwark than many battle-ships.

M. C. S.

HINDHEAD,
August 1928.

Note

I DESIRE to thank very cordially the many people who have kindly helped me by their comments, criticisms or proof corrections of this book. While none of them are in any degree responsible for the whole (as I have gone my own determined way over some points one or other would have liked me to suppress), yet the pages are benefited by their corrections and I am deeply grateful to them for their general approval and agreement.

First among those I must thank comes my husband, HUMPHREY V. ROE, whose help with the manuscript and proof has been invaluable. The expert reading of my manuscript by Tolstoy's famous biographer, AYLMER MAUDE, was most helpful. I must specially thank two representative members of the medical profession from whom I have had helpful criticisms. I have stuck to my guns about a few points, but have only been too pleased to accept several emendations with gratitude. To Dr. MAXWELL TELLING, M.D., B.S., F.R.C.P., Professor of Medicine, Leeds; and Dr. GILBERT R. A. ARMSTRONG, B.A. (Oxon.), M.B., Ch.B. (Edin.), I tender cordial thanks. Dr. Telling was so kind as to write: "The book as a whole will be of tremendous use, though it reaches out after a higher ideal than even did the original volume. It carries the education of the public a stage further. Your whole book is a succession of

practical pieces of advice to remove the various
stumbling-blocks that may, and frequently do,
arise; many of them small matters which, if properly
understood, can be dealt with and will then permit
the consummation of marriage in happiness enduring to its last stages with a beauty transcending
its beginning because more spiritualised and
strengthened by years of happy experience and
knowledge. If I have been of any help in my detailed
criticisms, I shall be very glad to have had even the
smallest finger-tip in the pie of your offering to a
hungry world."

Of all the many encouraging and touching
tributes to the difficult work I am trying to do which
have reached me in recent years, nothing has
pleased me more than the cordiality shown me by
innumerable members of the medical profession.
A few of the "old school" powerful in office give
some slight substance to the error transmitted by
opponents that "the medical profession is hostile"
to my work. But I know better! Ringing in my ears
are the repeated and heartening cheers of packed
audiences composed entirely of medicals in one
after another of the Medical Schools and at Branch
Meetings of the British Medical Association. Their
appreciation and cordiality is more vital than the
opposition of a few.

I am confident that the innumerable doctors who
have kindly recommended *Married Love* to their
patients will recognise in this volume a useful
successor.

October 1928.   M. C. S.

Chapter I

A Common Sadness

"Marriage requires to be transformed, because everything around it is transformed."—FINOT.

EVERY true lover desires that love shall endure. In young lovers, the conviction flowers easily and spontaneously that their new passion is not only unique in its individual beauty, but is eternal, more lasting than life itself. Yes, even to-day, although the young achieve their mating under increasing difficulties, owing to the ever-growing vastness of cities and the individual peculiarities of civilised people, nevertheless the majority of young people love spontaneously and naturally, and hope with the eternal hope of youth.

It has been brought to my notice over and over again that an uneasiness lurks in the recesses of the minds of even the most romantic and instructed married lovers. They fear the existence of some *natural* law predestined in the end to work against them and destroy their mutual attraction. They wonder whether all the help afforded by knowledge such as I give in *Married Love* merely, at the best, secures a few years of happiness, and whether time will give that cruel law its inevitable innings and they will grow apart.

That so many pairs of happy lovers should have turned into drabby tolerant married couples, or should learn positively to detest, or even to fear each other as the years pass, saddens us all.

One cannot take up a newspaper nowadays without finding articles, stories or letters, written on the assumption that, after the passing of some years, nearly every marriage will become dreary or worse. All this has a hypnotic effect on people who cannot altogether avoid the influences of "crowd sentiment." One feels that it could not take root and persist if there were not some basis of fact, or at any rate supposed fact, giving it substance. There must be something more fundamental than the accidents of time and ailments to overturn deeply rooted love, for one sees how negligible such externals may be when passion endures.

A generally felt anticipation seems to be:—
That the very basis of marriage is thus

attacked by the "inevitable" failure to persist, of the mutual sex attraction. That it gradually fades out altogether as does a child's sandcastle on the shore, eaten away little by little by the advancing tide of indifference the waves of which lap forwards after each act of union in the trough of despondency or indifference which follows it.

It is widely assumed that in the path of those who have been married for some time stalks the apparently unconquerable dragon the doom of all mating humanity for centuries whose form and ramifications are hinted at in the Latin proverb: "Post coitum omne triste," or "Omne animal post coitum triste." (After coitus all are depressed.)

This conception has coloured innumerable creative minds; tinged with asceticism, pessimism, gloom or ribaldry the works of great masters of literature; afforded the theme of plays and poems; woven itself into the social conventions. Many a doubtful joke and story hinges upon the universal acceptance of the idea. Indeed so ingrained in human consciousness is it, so fundamentally entrenched that the vast majority of adult men really believe it. I did not deal with it, or even hint at it in *Married Love*, the book for happy youth, yet the dragon's plangency was somewhat weakened by that book. It is time it was slain by serious people and its suggestive power for evil shattered.

The chapters of this new book may at first sight appear unrelated, yet I trust they will all do their share of dragon-slaughter.

To expand the terseness of the Latin phrase so as fully to express explicitly all that it subtly implies would require many pages. As was once said to me briefly by a married man, it is that: "All the world knows after the sex act, the man is weakened and disgusted and turns away from woman for a time until his natural lust returns."

In other words it is the idea, which the experience of many people would appear to confirm, that, after the marriage act (the union of the man and the woman), the eagerness and the vitality of the man are reduced: he has used up some of his energy, and he has to recuperate thereafter. This implies that the act of union, although it may have been consummated as a result of an intense urge, and is a natural physiological demand of his body, necessitates an expenditure rather than a gaining of energy on the part of the man, and has left him with his forces temporarily reduced.

Few have combated this assumption. It is true that in his monumental work *Studies in the Psychology of Sex*, Dr. Havelock Ellis does not subscribe to this "popular fallacy," but devotes half a page to emphasise his view that "under reasonably happy circumstances there is no pain, or exhaustion, or sadness, or emotional revulsion. The happy lover's attitude toward his partner is not expressed by the well-known sonnet (cxxix) of Shakespeare:—

> 'Past reason hunted, and no sooner had
> Past reason hated.'

He feels rather with Boccaccio that the kissed mouth loses not its charm,

> 'Bocca bacilata non perde ventura.' "

How to secure and maintain the "reasonably happy circumstances" he does not tell a world deeply hungering for the information. I propose to attempt to give it such help. That it desperately needs new light on the problem of permanence of sex love in marriage leaps at one's heart.

Few men are quite as frank as was Lord X. before I wrote this book, when in the privacy of a *tête-à-tête* in his own house, he turned upon me with bitterness for having told womanhood in my book *Married Love* of the physical joys of marriage. "What have you done?" he exclaimed. "You have broken up the home; you have let women know about things which only prostitutes ought to know; once you give women a taste for these things, they become vampires, and you have let loose vampires into decent men's homes. When we men want that sort of thing—a woman who knows how to enjoy herself in sex life—we go to prostitutes at our own times when we feel like it. We do not want that sort of thing in our own homes. The wife should be the housekeeper and make the home a place of calm comfort for a man. Instead of that you have made my home a hell: I cannot meet the demands of my wife now she knows. If you create these vampire women, you will rear a race of effeminate men." Continuing with fury, did not this man, assailing true love, scourging me as its exponent, really reveal his own debased ideas of woman captive and enslaved in a home? For him woman should be deprived not only of the enjoyment of true sex union, but of its health-giving balance, its vitalising power, and the very joyous sense of equality with her mate.

Woman, according to him, is to be the housekeeper, the breeder, but never his mate, his joyous companion. Selfishly he goes to the prostitute whom he can pay at his own time to simulate passion and play with him in any filthy manner that his debased taste craves.

This man is elderly. I suppose he would be in enthusiastic agreement with Acton, the classic "authority," who once said: "Happily for society the majority of women are not very much troubled with sex feelings of any kind."

The concomitant of this is evident. The sacramental and mutual character of true union is overlooked. Naturally where lust and not true love urge the pair together, after that brief union the man experiences a lack of interest, shading in some into a repulsion. In others there may even be a positive fear of the partner in union owing to the feeling that the woman has robbed them of something. Such unions do rob both man and woman of the very best and highest aspects of sex life.

One could easily fill many books if one began to elaborate and reproduce in its manifold forms and presentation throughout the romantic and scientific literature, medical treatises, common talk of country folk, and the ribald jests of the slums and the music-hall, the idea behind "Post coitum omne triste."

And now I challenge it!

I challenge, not that it is generally considered to be a fact: that is obvious! I challenge the very existence of the fact itself. I deny that it is a *fact* in a scientific sense. It is a phenomenon based on ignorance and folly and the hypnotism of custom. It is *not* an inherent physiological and inevitable result of the unions of an enlightened and instructed race of lovers.

I challenge the ages and the men of all ages! I tell them that this false "fact" of theirs has warped, coloured and injured their lives, weakened their powers, cut at the roots of their love, eaten like a canker into their respect for womanhood, blasted and desolated homes. It is not a true fact when viewed by science. It is a chimera bred by ignorance, haunting the cloudy miasmic swamps of tradition.

Confusion and misapprehension have arisen from the hasty misunderstanding of countless men and women. Having themselves flouted Nature by thwarting her intentions; injured Nature by bending her to their will; acting wrongly because they were misinformed, they plunged themselves, and involved almost the entire human race in an intricate web of grievances and distresses—needlessly.

Some couples happily escape what is generally considered the common fate of

A Common Sadness

mated mankind. Theirs are the lifelong happy
marriages. They are few. One can scarcely
take up the day's journal at any time without
some reference to the rarity of happiness in
marriage lasting over many years. When the
lambent exceptions are commented upon, the
suggestion is that there had been some
chance combination of qualities in this man
and woman, specially favoured by the Gods
of fate, so that they have loved lastingly. If
questioned, the pair will generally attribute
their success in marriage to some extraneous
circumstances, or simply claim that they
loved and knew how to love; giving so little
explanatory addition that the enquiring mul-
titude is left as uninstructed as before. The
existence of such couples is a fortunate
chance. It is one of the objects of this book
vastly to increase the number of such couples,
and not only to challenge the desolating
"Post coitum omne triste," but to show in
detail how it is wrong, and how that wrong
may be righted.

There is nothing in the world which the
human heart so desires as a steady home life,
lasting and enduring love, and the radiance
of inner unity and mutual delight. No excuse
is needed for attempting to contribute something which should help multitudes to secure
these treasures. Who can doubt that the sta-

bility of the nation depends on the health and *happiness* of its homes. While we are human beings inhabiting this world, surely even the most presumptuous of us cannot claim to be anything higher than human. The success of our experience in life depends on an intricately interwoven but nicely balanced adjustment and satisfaction of the needs and requirements of all three factors—body, mind and spirit.

Throughout this book, I shall not attempt to disentangle these factors and to deal first in one chapter with one, and then in another with the other, for their actions and reactions are all interwoven. If I appear to emphasise the body, it is because it can be directly reached by material aids and thus assisted to be a more perfect instrument of the soul. In all chapters I will try to clarify what seem to me the salient points in the aspect of sex love therein considered. Just as when writing *Married Love* it was essential to set out the anatomical and physiological details of the sex organs, and simply to state the direct facts of coitus: so, to consider the present theme it will be essential to deal with further material facts about, and the conduct of, the act of coitus. Coitus is the kernel of physical marriage. The minutiæ of the way in which sex union between man and woman is conducted give rise to other reactions, branching into many ramifications of human thought and effort.

In *Married Love* I explained why I demanded the *wooing* of the wife and the attainment of the orgasm for her as well as for her husband. The recognition, now almost universal, that this—ten years ago so audacious a demand—is woman's legitimate right is a great step forward. But now I demand something more, another step forward in marital conduct. This time the benefit is more directly a gain to the man than to the woman, but, as in all things concerning the mutual partnership of marriage, the gain for one is the enrichment of both.

In my opinion, to establish an enduring passion in a lasting marriage it is necessary to uproot various physical faults commonly practised which lie behind the Latin phrase "Post coitum omne triste." I shall come to grips with that in Chapter VIII after probing some of the many factors of established marriage as distinct from the early honeymoon days.

Chapter II

Rare Contentment

"A thing of beauty is a joy for ever."—KEATS.

ONE hears so often the stupid phrase "Human nature never changes," that it is well worth while reminding ourselves that there is no expression of vitality in the world which has changed so rapidly as human nature, save its attendants and friends the domestic animals. There is no form of wild life, no "animal nature" that changes as does human nature. The ants and the spiders, the fish and the squirrels, all other wild creatures persist in being very much what they were a million years ago: but, are men and women, reared in the city, conscious both of the thoughts of the ages past, and of the words spoken at the other side of the world but a moment or two earlier, to be compared with their forefathers scarcely evolved from the ape-like stage, living in trees, gibbering without human speech?

To ask the question is to answer it—to expose to ridicule one of the commonest falsities of everyday speech with which thoughtless people so stupidly colour the attitude of society towards itself. When, parrot-like, "Human nature never changes" is repeated glibly by persons who are "educated" on artificial lines without a knowledge of man's true place in the Universe, they are merely helping to keep humanity bound in false shackles. The barbaric attitude of mind of the primitive peasant to his work-mate, of the mediæval overlord to his enemies' daughters made his in capture, are each expressions of sex-customs utterly different from those now prevalent. The "human nature" which could tolerate or enjoy some aspects of such relations does not even exist in most people to-day, so radically altered has it been. Altered by evolution into something higher.

There is not only to-day, but there has been for thousands of years, so rich and so conflicting a range of variety in "human nature" that it is absurd to generalise about it. Yet I will venture to say that I think there are now more who love on a high plane of equality and delicate courtesy than there have ever been before.

Although here and there in the fleeting

civilisations of the past are records of highly evolved individuals, and lives which have almost touched in their mutual love experience the degree of comradeship and mental and spiritual understanding that now exists quite frequently between man and woman, those of old were but scattered members of a vanguard in advance of their time. The present is the first period in the history of the world when any *large* number of the total population find themselves surrounded by the necessary mental environment to make possible the erogamic life. (See p. 16.)

Finot was right when he said: "The beloved Woman has changed her soul" and "woman is loved frequently for different reasons from those of former days. The lovers do not perceive this, but lovers, from time immemorial, have been blind."

I have often felt the need for a word to express this. An idea can only take root in the consciousness when it is given a material body in a dictionary. For the modern relation between man and woman, mated or living in the innumerable interdependencies, the mutual obeisances, the mutual respects which are not paralleled at all in the sex relation of the primitive peoples or in the debased lives of the violently depraved, a clean, fresh, subtle word was wanted. For this elevated interplay between man and woman I proposed the word *erogamic*[1] life.

Erogamic is a new word coined for the purpose of crystallising what I feel is a vital idea that is in our midst though yet scarcely recognised. The word is derived from the Greek: *eros*—love, and *gamos*—marriage or mating. I minted it with the intention that it shall designate that noble flower of the duality of human life, the mating and relation together of man and woman in all three planes—physical, mental and spiritual.

The erogamic life is that which we who would elevate and enrich the relation between man and woman, hold up as a standard. The physiological aspects of normal sex we all share with the animals as a physical basis in our lives; for the evolved interplay of man and woman we can speak of erogamic life and leave the ugly slimy sounding word "sexual" to those who still roll in the filth and who delight in the unclean echoes of the centuries.

I desire to free this idea in all its potential

[1] This was in my book *Sex and the Young*, p. 190, London, 1926. Various causes have prevented this book reaching so wide a circle as my others, and this has grieved me because I particularly desired to help the young *through their elders*. The book is now being published by my usual publisher and so may reach the hands of those for whom I intended it.

power and beauty. Hence I should like the fresh word for the fresh and beautiful concept (essentially characteristic of this century) of nobly and completely mated man and woman, to replace the soiled and bedraggled collection of ideas and themes at present lumped together under the word "sexual." The world has rightly sickened of "talk of things sexual." The very word is itself sickening and rouses many ancient antagonisms. That nobler thing which has grown, almost unobserved, in our midst is a great and beautiful fact which we can sense better when it is defined and described in a word giving a clear, fresh picture, free from primitive obsessions.

Throughout this book when I mean the nobler thing I shall speak of erogamic life. For dictionary purposes I defined the new word erogamic as "All that relation, in cultivated communities, between man and woman as mated pair, which involves their mutual interplay and interdependencies in physical, mental, and spiritual life."

All the higher aspects of the love of man and woman, however, although they intensify and heighten the ecstasy mutually afforded by the sexes to each other if they are based firmly on a broad and solid foundation of physical rightness, tend to disturb the balance and to increase the difficulties and dangers of those whose physical existence is not firmly rooted in the sweet earth of the body. I ask my readers to remember that, although I emphasise physical points, it is simply because for so long these have been ignored, neglected, and misrepresented. A knowledge of the physical basis of sex life between man and woman has almost ceased to exist save among experts. These experts, alas, are almost all warped and rendered myopic by their continual encounters with diseased, abnormal, and suffering examples of humanity. For the healthy in mind and body wholesome truth and right thinking are scarcely to be obtained.

Men and women need each other in every aspect of human life. The mere mingling of the two sexes in the social and semi-intellectual occupations of society, in the concert hall, the university, the office, and the club more closely in the dance and the athletic ground does to-day for each sex a good deal that is very necessary and that, long ago, could only be done by marriage. To-day men and women are both the richer for the free and frequent association with the other sex which modern life affords. Consider the position of the old-fashioned schoolmistress in a "ladies' seminary" for instance. When I was a little girl such a one told me of the flutter and physical thrill the intrusion of

c

a man in her drawing-room made when she
was young. And men who go far afield to
outposts remote from women have told me
how the craving for woman is to some extent
satisfied, at any rate soothed, by the mere
presence even of an elderly woman in the
farmhouse. They would travel miles only to
sit in the kitchen near her while she cooked.
I have a half-formed theory—no more, so
vague it is perhaps premature to mention it—
that men and women can affect and enrich
and to some degree interpenetrate each other
in some subtle way depending on electrical
or magnetic currents characterising each sex
and mutually affecting them. These are, of
course, invisible and are generally uncon-
sidered. I think such subtleties play a very
important part in life. I think their existence
is probably one of the reasons for the lack
of balance and unhealthiness which develop
in groups all of one sex, living without the
natural mingling with the other. Such single-
sexed communities as schools, nunneries, and
men at war are all starved for the *subtle* un-
conscious interchanges of a healthy mixed life.

Nowadays modern social life gives more of
that mingling of the sexes than we have known
for long. In a way that very fact places a
strain on marriage, because almost everything
for which people used to marry, except the

actual sex relation and parenthood, can now be experienced in the ordinary course of social life. The deeper and essential aspects of marriage therefore want stressing and understanding to-day more than they ever did.

In these modern days when friendships, mutual occupation, business, almost every phase of our civilised life, bring men and women together in innumerable ways, the only justification of marriage is the *mutual need* for and the *mutual enjoyment* in *sex union*.

If in that *marriage* partnership the two are so deeply and profoundly welded as they should be, and may be if they will but act rightly, then the mountains of minor miseries which so often burden people's lives disappear, float away in smoke. Jealousy, and all its ugliness and bitterness and discontent, will not find the soil in which to breed. How can it when *all* that the partner does, and is, and has, is, through the bodily transmission of joy, become a part of self? In the lives of a *happy* pair there isn't time or inclination to listen to all the petty social gossip and unpleasant scandals which jealousy and bitterness let loose upon society like a swarm of disease-carrying flies. I know one pair of truly welded married lovers for instance, each of whom for a couple of months went away on solitary expeditions, the man with a young woman to inhabit a mountain hut and make magnetic observations at a high altitude—solitary in that hut for all those weeks, and the wife tramping with a party of men on a different scientific quest. Neither even *thought* of their companions in those occupations with mating thoughts of sex—neither even had a shadow of objection to the opportunities offered the other, and both met like bride and bridegroom at the close of their separation. True love *welds* and *purifies*. The bodily meetings interchange until their lives are welded together as was described so briefly and with profound truth in the Bible: "They twain shall be one flesh."

Since first *Married Love* was published, ten years have passed with such amazing rapidity that it seems in some ways but a few weeks since, by publishing that book I let loose upon my shoulders an avalanche of demand, enquiry and appeal from humanity in every country of the world for just that deeper probing of marriage which I postulate. In these ten years I have garnered many facts about human life, and of them I wish particularly to emphasise (because I think it cannot be said too explicitly or too emphatically) the fact that, in marriage, as

distinct from any other human relationship,
the bedrock of lasting happiness, of security,
of health in every respect, lies in a proper
physical adjustment of the two persons, and
a proper physical management of their mutual
experiences of union. Marriage differs from
every other relation possible: it is, and must
always be, distinct from all the other affec-
tional relationships. Under happy conditions
the married pair keep house together; but
the housekeeping is really irrelevant. The
reason for marriage must be, not the house
but the heart.

Sometimes in the cynical "modern" novels,
plays or short stories, so prevalent to-day,
one reads that the married couple separated
for some trivial thing—because the woman
did not know how to pronounce difficult
words, or did not care for the scientific, or
artistic, "high-brow" occupation of her husband. I am certain that in real life no such
reason ever separated a couple who were
mutually in physical harmony. Where the
acts of coitus are rightly performed, the pair
can disagree, can hold opposite views about
every conceivable subject under the sun
without any ruffling or disturbance of the
temper, without any angry scenes or desire
to separate: They will but enjoy each
other's differences. Contrariwise I am sure

that they can have ninety-nine per cent. of all their other qualities and attributes in perfect harmony, and if the sex act is not properly performed; if they fail to adjust themselves to each other; if they are ignorant of the basic laws of union in marriage, all that harmony and suitability in other things will be of no avail, and they will rasp each other apart in sentiment, until they but endure each other for some extraneous motive, or they desire to part.

Long ago Balzac said very truly: "A husband and wife who are in the habit of occupying separate rooms are either beings apart, or they have found happiness. Either they hate or they adore each other." (*The Physiology of Marriage*, Engl. transl., privately printed, 1924.)

In this chapter let us presuppose that they adore each other, and that we watch them tenderly. A tear of sympathy will lurk near the corner of the eye of the observer. For adoration is sacred, and happiness brings tears to a sensitive mind.

We see the fortunate young couple blessed with children. We enjoy with them the exquisite panoramas of pearl and rose, of

dewy blossoms and celestial glances bestowed
by a child every hour of the day. There is no
time for these married lovers to think of
themselves or of any difficulties of their own.
They are carried along on the waves of
youth. No previous experience for either of
them has proved so rich in interest and
possibilities, no time so grandly surrounded
with a sense of opening vistas, as the years
which bring the successive births of little
ones, each welcomed by love and understanding.

The months of expectant motherhood have
been rendered as easy as they can be by
following the advice given in my book
Radiant Motherhood. The births of the
beloved babies spaced wisely, the means to
attain which are fully given in my book
*Contraception (Birth Control), its Theory,
History and Practice*. So that here I will not
touch at all on the many essential subjects
dealt with in those books, but assume that
all is right in these respects.

Arising from this deep physical unity grows
the home with all its spiritual comforts and
material conveniences. The husband and father
is not outside the nursery, but is most closely
and intimately a partner in all aspects of
parenthood. The children, born of love and
of the desire of each to see a repetition of the

beloved, stimulate the mental and spiritual growth of their parents. So that the home and the deep love which gave rise to it may endure even though illness or disaster may temporarily debar the parents from union. But it must not be forgotten that the home originated in love and to be maintained whole it must be carried on by *lovers*.

The need of the man and the woman for each other is in the terms of its highest expression not the need of the man for *a* woman, or the need of the woman for *a* man, but the need of each individual for its own mate—the mate who grows ever more and more deeply into the very nature of the being of each until the two have become one in the real old Biblical sense: "One flesh." Thus they form that higher unit of humanity, "the pair," rather than a couple of isolated individuals. This idea used to be expressed in a very beautiful old-English word, now fallen into disuse, which I should like to see revived, the human "duity" in contrast to God's Unity.

This duity, this unit composed of two like but dissimilar lives interlocked so as to make one unit existence, is an extremely important item in the social system of any State desiring permanence, continuity and stability. In a muddled half-conscious way, this is recognised by many of our current laws and customs, but unfortunately there is a tendency at present for "advanced" people to proceed towards the disintegration rather than the deeper cementing of the human duity. This seems to me essentially retrograde and I hope it is but a phase of evolution of the mind, the result of conclusions too hastily formed, the effervescence due to the pouring of new wine into old bottles. It is the stupid type of mistake often made when intellect, insufficiently equipped with superficial facts, tries to overturn some agelong fundamental truth. The intellect, indeed, is nearly always wrong. Yet it is often arrogantly conceited until another decade knocks its conclusion on the head. Then a new young sproutling of arrogance has in turn its own brief day, until perhaps more careful scientific thought and research come in to show that some ancient truth was profoundly right after all, and humanity may be at last allowed to return to its old prejudices and likings reassured by intellect that they are correct.

An illuminating illustration of this is found in the attitude of the simple housewife and ordinary uneducated person towards butter. A decade or two ago, modern science, cock-a-hoop at having discovered margarine and the "scientific" substitutes for butter, was urging them upon the housewife for domestic use, assuring her that they were "just as good." Those who had some education, whose intellects in my opinion had ceased to be responsive to their innermost instincts, were delighted. The result was that in the upper class and middle class homes the mothers would even provide margarine in the nursery, although they were cowed by their uneducated cooks so that they dared not give it in the kitchen. Thus *Punch* and all the comic papers were full of jests about how the uneducated demanded and had to have butter, while superior persons were in a similar manner demanding margarine. But what did a little deeper work in science do? Discovered that the cooks, the common persons and the simple housewives were right after all, and that in butter there are subtle but immensely important vitamins; that margarine as originally supplied was no true substitute for butter, giving only the chemical oils, but failing entirely to contain the precious vitamins, which are of vital importance in the nursery. Now the intellectual person glibly chatters "vitamins," and butter is restored to the position that it held in the uneducated housewife's esteem one hundred years ago.

So in human love! The agelong instinct of the sweeter and sounder sort of humanity has

been for a lifelong love and enduring monogamic devotion, romantic in youth, rapturous
in early marriage and matured in a serene old
age. This ideal must survive though smirched
by the nastiness of religious ascetics, attacked
on all sides by the corruption and difficulties
of social life, eaten into by the worm in the
bud, and the canker at the heart caused by
ignorance of physiological truth which prudery
has so long forced on youth, sneered at by
the "intellectuals," the "advanced" who are
now trying to encourage humanity to be
"superior" to it. But I trust and believe the
day of its enemies is done or nearly so. They
remind me of what was said by Walter Bagehot
(*Physics and Politics*, London, undated, new
ed.): "There is a great story of some African
Chief who expressed his disgust at adhering to
one wife, by saying it was 'like the monkeys.'
The semi-brutal ancestors of man, if they
existed, had very likely an instinct of constancy, which the African Chief, and others
like him, had lost."

Perhaps now we are evolved enough to
return to the phase of monogamic constancy
on a higher plane of understanding. At any
rate, it seems to me that scientific work is
already beginning to show that the ancient
instinctive ideal is right, and has a physiological basis which gives it a permanent

wholesomeness—a solid value—and I hope that the wheel of fashion will soon turn towards the REALLY *advanced* idea that the married pair is one enduring human *duty*, generated by romantic love, but bred, fostered and established by all the multitudinous aspects of the true erogamic life.

Even St. Paul recognised: "It is not good to defraud ye one of the other except for a season," and the home in which there is much defrauding of the other is a home tending to be slightly abnormal—built round a marriage which is beginning to take risks.

Dr. W. F. Robie, the wisest and most helpful of American sexologists, confirms what I had expressed about the sex relation in *Married Love* and *Wise Parenthood* in 1918, and said, even more explicitly and emphatically, in his *Sex and Life* in 1920: "There is a notion prevalent among those who theorise rather than observe, that sex relations between man and wife should be for the purpose of begetting children only. No more erroneous, pernicious, or injurious idea can be entertained by the young woman entering matrimony. . . . The social value of intercourse between man and wife is as necessary and legitimate as the procreative value."

As the years pass, it is too often this

aspect of marriage (really its very kernel) which is neglected or in some way spoiled. There is not the slightest doubt that in most marriages after a decade or less some accident, hitch, misunderstanding, illness, or ignorance has generally interfered with the perfect harmony of the sex union and reduced or demolished its potentialities for good.

Some of the points dealt with in the chapters following may arise in almost any marriage, even one wisely founded, and unless they are handled with knowledge, they are likely to destroy the very bedrock on which that marriage is built.

Chapter III

Excessive "Virility"

"There may be too much of a good thing."—PROV.

A NUMBER of married women's lives
are rendered unduly difficult, even
somewhat abnormal, because their
husbands' demands for union are in excess
of what they themselves can give with spontaneous and mutual satisfaction. There are
some, though perhaps they are not average,
husbands, for instance, who insist on unions
more than once *every* day. (See Chapter
IX "Frequency" for more details.) Such
demands, even if made by true love, generally
result in the woman becoming the "slave of
man," as it is rather luridly described by the
feminists. On the other hand, her happiness
may be threatened by the knowledge that
her husband is unfaithful to her, and is im-
pelled to this by mere physical desire. A
woman's potential happiness in sex life is
deadened or killed outright by demands

which are so frequent and so regardless of her own needs and requirements that they crush spontaneity and happiness, and consequently invade the health.

A married couple may feel for each other a very real love, each aching to do the best for the other, and the last thing they desire is the breaking up of the home, but their harmony may be jeopardised by the encroachment on the wife's health and happiness of an excessive natural virility in her man. Many women gallantly try to meet it and *act* the daily part which they could, with natural and spontaneous happiness, really feel at less frequent times. Dissimulation, however, is a poor and shifty foundation for so important an edifice as love. Wherever possible something more real should be done to assist in the mutual adjustment. Here I will not repeat what I said in Chapter V in *Married Love*, but ask that if any couple feel the strain of a divergence in sex requirement, they will study that chapter and really try to practise what it teaches.

There will be some men, however, who are so "virile" that they find it impossible to conform to its advice. What then?

Of course, a great deal depends on the age of the man and the habits which have become established. If the man is young and very virile, has only been married for a few years, and really loves his wife, with the increasing understanding and sympathy, and the increasing stability given by the experience of union, there is every chance that he may instinctively reduce his demands as his nature is satisfied and balanced by union. His zest for passionate experience will somewhat quieten down as the years pass if he definitely wills to accomplish the mastery of his body.

Also I am coming to the conclusion that this fierce, at first almost insatiable desire for union, is often the result of an actual craving for *nourishment* in union somewhat parallel to, although less easy to demonstrate than in the sex-starved woman. So I ask men finding themselves in this predicament to read what I say on pages 46, 7 following and give the idea some consideration. It cannot be demonstrated as it can in women, but nevertheless I am much inclined to believe there is a closer parallel in nature between the deeper results of sex union in the two sexes than is generally supposed. I am also sure that one reason why some men inordinately crave for sex union is that they are really *hungry*. They do not get the profound satisfaction in union which they should because they snatch but a mouthful of the feast each time. Consider here also Chapter VIII of this volume.

In addition to the vital matters there considered, there are various quite simple practical means of assisting a little in reducing the urgency of repeated desire: A daily cold bath has long been recommended to healthy manhood, and part of the routine should be the daily retraction of the foreskin and thorough cleansing with soap and water, as well as the daily determination of the will to set aside extraneous stimulus. What composes such stimuli will have to be thought out by each man for himself, for the miscellaneous pictures and the varied concepts rousing potential desire are so numerous and so varied, and so often peculiar to an individual, that each must recognise for himself what he had best avoid.

On the other hand, if the man is thirty-five or over, and has been married some years and still has frantic sex stimulation several times a day at any pretty aspect of his wife which attracts him particularly, his is probably a case for a medical examination. He may be like Mr. B., whose wife was known to me intimately. A few years ago, before the sight of long silk stockings was quite so commonplace as it is to-day, Mr. B. used to go frantic with desire and entreat her to allow union at

D

any time of the day if he caught sight of even a few inches of her silk-clad calves. This made her perfectly miserable, although neither of the pair said a word about it to any medical adviser. In my opinion, it indicated that the man was probably an incipient case of enlarged prostate. He died of something else before I plucked up courage to speak of it, and her widowhood was a relief to her. It seems to me tragic that after a few years a girl who was deeply in love at first and was passionately adored should be glad to be a widow.

It is well known to the expert practitioners who specialise in urino-genital troubles that an enlarged prostate[1] may be incipient or slowly increasing for quite a number of years before such symptoms arise as cause the man to think of applying for medical assistance. Ordinary people, however, seem never to have heard of this. The fact that such enlargement causes an intensification of sex feeling; and that the repeated and almost frantic need for sex union is one of the symptoms of the earlier phases of prostatic enlargement, should be known to everyone. It is such useful knowledge that it ought to

[1] An accessory sex structure, a gland lying at the base of the male sex organs which gives out secretions forming part of the "ejaculate."

be quite widely and generally spread instead of being crammed into the furthest and dimmest recesses of the "hush-hush" about which we scarcely even whisper. Such enlargement explains phenomena which may worry and upset an otherwise happy household. In a man of forty or over, if an increase in desire or a very violent need for repeated union unexpectedly arises, it would be wise at once to have an examination of the prostate with a view to its correction if necessary. If neglected, prostatic enlargement is one of the most painful afflictions from which men suffer, and finally may become a very dangerous trouble.

In middle age, if it occurs at all, the enlargement is generally slow and in the earlier stages the man may really *enjoy* a degree of intensification of sex excitement which overpowers his wife, but appears to do him no harm.

If, on the other hand, the man is well into the sixties, and suddenly becomes, as some men do at that age, very markedly and excessively interested in sex matters, so that he may not find his wife, however complaisant, sufficient for his demands, he may be led to carry on silly flirtations or liaisons with young girls. This sometimes happens to, and distracts, blameless men devoted to their wives.

Such an expression of sex activity and apparent "virility" should certainly be looked into from a medical point of view as it is most likely to be correlated with enlarged prostate. At that age, if neglected, the man's time of enjoyment will be short. Surgeons who specially treat this subject emphasise the necessity of dealing with such enlargements before they become so great as to be dangerous or to necessitate a troublesome operation.

The demand for a simple "pill" or drug to solve all such troubles is astonishingly widespread. After lecturing to working-class audiences, in the question time, and even more when talking individually to members of the audience afterwards, I am surprised by the prevalence of the rumour that there are drugs which can safely be taken to reduce man's virility, and that such drugs act directly and only on the sex organs. I think it may not be out of place, even in a book specifically addressed to educated people, to explode this popular fallacy, and warn everyone that *no reliable drug of this nature exists*.

It is true, however, that certain lowering drugs are sometimes administered to men. I understand that in some prisons they are prescribed for specific reasons.

Several compounds of the *bromides* are used for this purpose. The bromides do not act directly and solely on the sex organs, but lower the tone of the whole nervous system, create a sense of weariness and lassitude, and are certainly not to be recommended unless under medical advice and for other purposes. As Dr. Havelock Ellis says (*Studies: Sex in Relation to Society*): "The bromides are universally recognised as powerful sex sedatives, but their influence in this respect only makes itself felt when they have dulled all the finest energies of the organism."

There is, in short, no specific drug known to me which it is safe for a man to prescribe for himself in the hope of reducing excessive virility.

A man inconveniently potent may with advantage avoid the use of alcohol so far as he can. Although alcoholic drinks do not enhance the actual potency of man, they do increase the desire for sex play and the craving for the act of union. Plain, simple living, cleanliness, healthy thoughts, wholesome but not excessive exercise, high ideals guiding a strong controlling will, and, in particular, hard *brain* work are also good allies against excessive venery.

Men are often told to spend hours exercising, and encouraged to play hard outdoor

games to tire themselves. But, so far as I can
collect evidence from men who do this, the
result is by no means what they set out to
attain. Indeed I think the idea that ordinary
athletics reduce the potentiality and the
sense of need for sex experience, is physiologically false. On the contrary, active exercise in the open air, particularly the sunny
air, directly stimulates sex potency. Several
articles in scientific journals have dealt with
the increase in potency and sex capacity in
bulls and stallions allowed outdoor exercise
instead of being shut up. An article in *Nature*
a few years ago included a brief statement
to the effect that exercise in the open
air and sunlight increased the sex potency
in man.

If the exercise is pursued so excessively as
to result in complete fatigue and an unhealthy
degree of exhaustion it may temporarily inhibit
sex desire with the other faculties, but is not
such a process quite as stupid and unwholesome as taking bromide drugs?

Where excessive desire for sex intercourse
is the outward symptom of a real craving for
the mutual enrichment which should go with
the rightly managed act of union, the best
of all "cures" for excessive sex desire is a
healthy, well balanced sex life, and coitus
performed in the *right* way. With this I deal

part of the man, the grievance of the woman is recognised both by Law and Church. (See also p. 54.)

But the girl, once made a wife, may thereafter have so scant a fare of the feasts of love as, literally, to be starved. What of a woman whose sex needs are such that she is left either below par and dissatisfied or really physically unhappy, almost ill, without frequent sex union, if her husband, while being not abnormally undersexed, yet is unable to meet her demands? Many women suffer frightfully in secret when placed in such a position in a "civilised" community. I am inclined to think that a large number of those in a "neurotic" condition, sufferers from sleeplessness, bad temper, indigestion and so on, are the victims of sex-deprivation. The profounder needs of their whole organisms are not being met.

Can anything be done? Of course *self* stimulus, or masturbation, is extremely common. It is used by married women whose husbands, having stimulated them, leave them in "mid-air" with no orgasm, causing nervous irritation. Masturbation is *not* the proper remedy, and a careful husband should secure orgasm for his wife. Masturbation is *always* unsatisfactory for various reasons, including those mentioned on the next page.

Another practical solution which some deprived women find is in Lesbian love with their own sex. The other, and quite correct name for what is now so often euphemistically called Lesbian love is homosexual vice. It is so much practised nowadays, particularly by the "independent" type of woman that I run a risk of being attacked because I call the thing by its correct name. One of the physical results of such unnatural relations is the gradual accustoming of the system to reactions which are arrived at by a different process from that for which the parts were naturally formed. This tends to unfit women for real union. If a married woman does this unnatural thing she may find a growing disappointment in her husband and he may lose all natural power to play his proper part. What I say on p. 65 applies also to women. No woman who values the peace of her home and the love of her husband should yield to the wiles of the Lesbian whatever the temptation to do so may be.

A very *very* few women have strong inborn tendencies of this type; most of those now indulging in the vice drifted into it lazily or out of curiosity and allowed themselves to be corrupted. This corruption spreads as an underground fire spreads in the peaty soil

of a dry moorland. Men with an excess of
the "feminine" qualities and "masculine"
women are, by the inherent bias given to their
emotions by their physical equipment, very
liable to enter into some degree or other of
the many possible relationships with their
own accredited sex. They may marry and yet
have disastrous homosexual entanglements.
Phases of the problems raised by such people
seem to me to call for recognition, yet they
lead us away from the theme of this book
into difficult realms. I do not want to discuss
homosexuality. Nevertheless I do want people
to understand what seems to me a vital
scientific argument against it untinged with
any of the simple, old-fashioned objections
now so often repudiated. The bedrock objection to it is surely that women can only
play with each other and *cannot* in the very
nature of things have natural union or supply
each other with the seminal and prostatic
secretions which they ought to have, and
crave for unconsciously.

Hence, homosexual excitement does not
really meet their need, for the physiological
fact (I have never yet seen it clearly stated
anywhere, but it is of the greatest importance
in a consideration of this problem) that,
apart from the kisses, endearment, flattery,
and love-making from her husband, a woman's

need and *hunger* for nourishment in sex union is a true physiological hunger to be satisfied only by the supplying of the actual molecular substances lacked by her system. Lesbian love, as the alternative, is NOT a real equivalent and merely soothes perhaps and satisfies no more than the surface nervous excitement. It does not, and by its nature it can never supply the actual physiological nourishment, the chemical molecules produced by the accessory glandular systems of the male. These are supplied to the woman's system when the normal act of union is experienced, and the man's secretions are deposited in her body together with the semen.

Dr. Maxwell Telling says about this: "I am not so near conviction about this as you appear to be, though I should like to be. To physiologists the true function of the prostatic fluid is still unknown: so far as I am aware it has not passed beyond the 'to dilate and give bulk to the semen' hypothesis of my student days. Contrasted with this your theory is at least attractive."

After I published *Wise Parenthood* some years ago, Sir William Arbuthnot Lane, the famous surgeon, told me of some interesting cases of his own which certainly seemed to indicate that part at least of the prostatic secretion is beneficially absorbed by the woman from the male ejaculate deposited in her vagina. This appeared to me to be of immense value in various ways, and to afford a key-explanation of a variety of phenomena. Since then I have followed up and studied the effect myself. I have come to the conclusion that there undoubtedly is a real physiological hunger for the chemical and complex molecular substances found in the accessory glands of the male, which can be supplied to women who unconsciously feel their need and show it in the apparently irrelevant but really quite direct way of inviting sex union in what appears excessive amounts from their mates. Or, sometimes, from lovers in addition to their husbands.

Such women are constantly sneered at or laughed at or made the butts of ignorant and vulgar jokes—but who has studied and helped them? Just a few medical men have "cured" a few of them as private patients by giving them certain glandular extracts. I know of no fair and kindly and open consideration of their needs. I think a frank and fundamental statement of the facts will do something to alter public opinion and clean up the fœtid atmosphere round the whole subject.

It has been found possible to prepare some
at least of the very molecular compounds really
nourishing to the woman's system, and which
she lacks and requires. These may be prepared
so as to preserve their chemical qualities, and
presented in such a way that they can be
swallowed by the mouth in ordinary gelatine
capsules. These capsules are just like those in
which many other medicines are prescribed
and taken in order to meet a great range and
variety of requirements in modern civilised
people.

Some medical practitioners administer such
glandular extracts by direct *injection* instead
of by the mouth, but I do not at all advise
injection for a great variety of reasons which
would take one too far to discuss. But one
simple reason may be readily grasped: We
cannot by any human process exactly simulate the way these glandular extracts naturally
enter the blood and lymph streams by
infinitesimal amounts *continuously*. The best
we can do is to take several small doses a
day, and to do this we can, without too great
a strain on the memory, manage, say, to
swallow a capsule three times daily, and
carry this on for several months. But can one
possibly ask or expect a busy medical practitioner to give his time and attention to
administer three injections a day for months

to an individual who is approximately well
any way, and only requires better "balance"
and "toning up"?

Moreover, who (even if the time could be
spared) would choose to be injected three
times a day for months if it could be avoided?
No healthy minded person.

Some practitioners formerly having tried
makes of extracts for use by the mouth which
proved unsatisfactory, distrust all such. But
there are now available reliable ones, and
without doubt their manufacture will rapidly
improve till all and not only a few firms can
supply satisfactory substances. I cannot refrain
from urging all my readers to avoid every
possible puncture of the skin. *Never* be
injected with anything if it is possible to
avoid it. There may be times in acute and
specific *disease* or threatened disease when
injection is not to be avoided, but I am not
now discussing *disease* at all.

In view of much vague and hysterical talk
on the subject of "glands" and especially
"monkey glands" (see also Chapter VII,
p. 112.) I want to make it clear that I am not
proposing the use of monkey glands at all
and do not in any circumstances recommend
them.

I should like my readers to realise how, by
our unnatural ideas about eating, we deprive

our systems of many parts of the animals which help to keep wild animals healthy, just as we lose all sorts of valuable mineral salts by throwing away the water in which we have been boiling vegetables. Then our systems may find a lack of, say, phosphorus compounds or iron compounds. When we lack these minerals we at once (if we are wise) reform our way of life, and meanwhile to restore ourselves swallow some mineral compounds in the form of "medicine" to supply to our alimentary canals the compounds from which our system is suffering a shortage; these are transmitted to the blood or lymph streams and thus supplied to the various tissues requiring these chemical molecules. Our cells then, successfully, carry on their work again. Now it has recently been discovered that by careful laboratory technique certain more complex chemical molecules given out by the various glands, can be isolated and "extracted" and specially prepared so that they too can be swallowed as "medicine." When it becomes evident that one or more of these types of chemical compounds is lacking they can be swallowed, enter the alimentary canal, and thence are transmitted to the blood or lymph streams and thus supplied to the various tissues requiring these chemical molecules. Our cells then, successfully, carry on their work again. The compounds are quite harmless and are effective.

Quite apart from the emotional loss in the absence of romance and sentiment, the sex-starved woman, in my opinion, is one whose system is not supplied with the necessary amount of certain complex chemical molecules produced in the prostatic glands. If then she will swallow the properly prepared extracts of these glands in suitable quantities for her own requirements, she should, by nourishing her system properly as it demands, not only enhance its general physiological condition, but mitigate the distressing *social* symptoms involved.

For some sex-starved women the prostatic extract alone is very effective, sometimes prostatic and orchic extract should be mixed. For others, those for instance with a markedly "run down" condition, the addition of chemical compounds of glycero-phosphates of calcium and other elements are useful. (See Appendix A, No. 1.)

It is very important that the extracts should be expertly and freshly made, and I trust the above clear statement of the *why* of the usefulness of such preparations will not lead women to take dry tablets and all kinds of "patent medicine" or quack nostrums which are soon sure to, if they do not already, abound on the market. Such a subject is too often surrounded by so much mystery that both the patient and the practitioner are shy of approaching or discussing it, and hence advice from commercial firms and quacks is often taken instead of proper medical advice. I do urge everyone to go only to reliable practitioners about such subjects. I feel that possibly the open and simple explanations given in this book may make it easier than it has been hitherto for people needing such help to go to their own doctors for the prescriptions. I do urge everyone *not* to take these or any prescriptions in the book without consultation with their medical attendant, and also I urge them not to increase the prescribed dose. It is such a common mistake to imagine that because one capsule or pill or tea-spoonful of anything is prescribed and seems to do good, that two or more of the same will do more good. An increased dose may often not only fail to do more good but may do active harm by upsetting the glandular balance in a fresh direction.

To take into the alimentary canal as nourishment chemical compounds of which our artificial mode of life deprives us is not only simple common sense, but is to conform to the custom we indulge in at every meal—

E

eating what we need to carry on our life-functioning.

The idea of *eating* to avoid fornication may appear—perhaps like all the new ideas of science it actually is—startling.

On consideration I think it will be realised by humanity not only as sound common sense, but also as a clean, wholesome, unexciting way of disposing of one of the most agonising, torturing worries of body and spirit which has burdened the shoulders of life's struggling pilgrims till they have sweated and panted and agonised in prayer. Eat—wisely. Lo! the burden will be lightened and may even roll off, and a once tormented woman can step lightly and happily forward.

Such nourishing capsules to assuage the sex hunger in deprived women should be of great use to three types of the strongly sexed:

(1) The loving wife accustomed to sex union with her husband in marriage, who is parted from him perforce when one of them is in a far country or they are separated owing to business or perhaps by the illness of one of the married pair.

(2) Then, too, there are women, whose husbands may be with them, and may be doing their "duty" (as it is sometimes rather crudely called), yet who find that insufficient to meet the needs of the personal equation.

They may with advantage supplement the amounts of glandular secretion which they obtain so as to meet their specially high requirements by taking these capsules at intervals when they feel the need.

(3) Then, too, there are those who are unmarried, and who at periodic intervals feel the passionate need of sex union, and yet, having a moral sense well developed and a recognition of the present social code, hesitate to have union outside marriage, and suffer (some of them suffer excessively) at recurrent intervals. Many such women would be definitely helped by taking such capsules for two or three days at the times of such spontaneous sex excitement.

This book is for the married, so here I do no more than point out their obvious value to strongly sexed unmarried women who desire to lead chaste lives.

I think such utilisation of the advances of modern science and the employment of glandular compounds for this purpose is one of the most potentially useful and socially valuable applications of modern research.

The report of a medical practitioner may be of interest here. He used prostatic extract for "an obscure nervous condition in an unmarried woman aged 35 years." "For several years she has suffered from what was termed by a neurologist, who examined her, 'sexual neurasthenia.' She also had melancholia and tachycardia." She took prostatic gland extract for two months and "she is very much improved. Her nervous and mental symptoms have cleared up, the pulse rate has reduced from 110 to 80; she has a cheerful outlook on life and her friends remark upon the wonderful change in her."

There is no doubt at all that numbers of unbalanced, sex-starved women in a community cannot fail to be a source of friction to others, and certainly of dissatisfaction and unhappiness to themselves.

It is perfectly right and proper that priests and pastors should preach continence and self-control. I too advise the use of both these, and indeed every mental aid to a well-balanced sex life. Yet doubtless as the truth is understood, it will increasingly be recognised that where there is a definite physiological deficit, a physiological hunger for certain chemical molecules, you might as well dangle a sugar cake in front of a child starving for its dinner and tell it not to cry but to exercise self-control, as to preach self-control unaided by physiological nourishment to a human being whose sex-system cries out for chemical molecules. Science can now isolate and supply the molecules suited to that system. Would it not be cruel to withhold that knowledge from use? It is a different thing to preach self-control to a nature reasonably nourished. For the first time in history our generation finds it possible to give some practical help to those naturally so strongly sexed that "self-control" becomes almost a physical impossibility through the frantic urge of physiological starvation. They may by quietly swallowing the glandular compounds they lack, assist themselves to become devout, and less the slave of their nature's demands for the enjoyment of the other sex. So much the better for mankind. Warped strivings and "kicking against the pricks" have never helped humanity forward. But a wise use of Nature's potential riches brings abundant rewards.

Chapter IV

Under-sexed Husbands

"That Power by which we are drawn we know as Love; but the fact that we are drawn, the fact that we must grow towards union, proves separateness; and the separation of those that long to be together is pain."—
Times Lit. Suppl. Leader, 1928.

RARE, but less rare than is generally imagined, is the completely impotent husband. He makes a normal marriage impossible. Yet strangely, his state may exist even for years undetected. Wives suffer in such marriages without realising why. Others equally unaware of any departure from the normal, may even be not at all unhappy. Strange as it may seem, an impotent man may be married, even for a large number of years, without unhappiness in the home on the part of either spouse. I know of one husband and his wife who were married for eleven years without either even suspecting that anything was in the least unusual in their marriage, the wife being quite content and thinking all was normal! My Solicitor also told me that he knew of other cases, one where, after twenty years, the wife, who was still a virgin, discovered then for the first time the nature of the unusual relation between her husband and herself. To consider such exceptional marriages would lead us too far astray from the main theme of this book, which is to help those who are normal or nearly so, to secure the utmost success and happiness possible in their marriage.

Yet it might help unlucky women to know how others feel who are in the position of Mrs. M.:—"I have been married five years and am still *virgo intacta* though both my husband and I passionately long for children. My beloved man is nearly 40 and he has no sex desires at all. He has tried to perform his marital obligations to me but he cannot get his organ to act at all and as the continual unsuccessful attempts upset me very much we now do not even try. I persuaded him to see a doctor who examined him thoroughly and pronounced that he was quite normally formed and his organs were perfectly healthy and capable of functioning but that his instincts were remarkably inactive. The doctor told him it wasn't anything to bother about and that it would probably 'come right' and if it didn't it wouldn't injure me in any way to have to live a platonic life. We are just tremendously fond of each other and we sleep together—and I can't tell you how his caresses and close proximity rouse all the normal instincts in me leaving me sleepless and agitated for hours and consequently I'm afraid somewhat irritable the next day."

For such couples I should advise a good holiday *apart* during which time the woman took the extracts described on p. 48 and the man those on p. 73. The man should take the extracts steadily for quite three months before attempting union unless in the meantime desire naturally welled up. He should continue the extracts for some time even after health appeared to be perfect.

There are many quite average sort of men whose type of sex life is the reverse of that considered in the last chapter, and so there must be many couples who will find something useful in the following brief notes on various aspects of the deficit of normal sex in man.

It should be made clear that impotence in sex union and complete sterility, i.e., absence of living spermatozoa, are two quite distinct states, and that both or either of them may be temporary or permanent.

In the ordinary way, sex desire and the power to accomplish union represent the co-ordinated results of that immensely complex organism, the human body, and it will be easily recognised that illness, disease, or a failure to act properly by any part of the body, may react on the sex powers. Thus pain or digestive disturbance or other temporary accidents or injuries which have no direct bearing on the sex organs often have temporary effects, reducing the sex vitality. Most of these trifles will naturally right themselves with time, an ordinary tonic and common sense.

Certain accidental injuries to the nerves, however, are likely to have a more direct and serious effect on the sex powers. In men blows or other injuries to the spine (such as may be experienced through a fall in the hunting-field, or wounding in warfare, or other form of accident), involving those spinal nerves which control the sex organs, may leave the man not only temporarily, but more or less permanently, incapable of a normal sex life. The effects appear in a variety of rather subtle ways, which will not in the least affect the vitality and motility of the actual spermatozoa—(that is the male germinating cells)—yet may inhibit or interfere with the erection or the normal power of

ejaculation and thus render sex union difficult
or impossible. Similarly, without the accident
of an actual blow or injury, prolonged and
very great mental strain, such as was experienced by men suffering from shell shock,
or those very sensitive to the horrors of the
war, led to a reaction which amounted almost
to sex impotence in a number of men. Some of
this was physiologically real and some induced
by imagination, i.e. what I have called "phan-
tasmal - impotence." Dr. Maxwell Telling
tells me he has frequently encountered in
such cases the idea that intercourse was
harmful to them and so abstinence was
enforced. Some of the simpler shock cases
dated their cure from the time they obtained
and followed contrary advice. It is an emer-
gence of the idea prevalently held by men
that sex union is really enervating and
exhausting to the male—a lie trailing so many
important reactions that it wants "nailing up"
conspicuously.

Hence for a good many years after the
war, and even still, some wives have to give
special consideration to their husbands injured
directly or indirectly in the war in this
fashion. Many such wives were naturally not
acquainted with the causes of the marital
weakness in their husbands. As such a result
was generally overlooked even by the medical

profession that is not surprising. There have,
I am sure, from what I have learned from
sufferers, been many needlessly heartbroken
wives who suspected infidelity when they
found their men on returning from the war
were no longer eager for intercourse, perhaps
no longer even capable of consummating sex
union with them. Those who were humble
of heart wept secretly at their own failure to
hold a dear husband; the harsher and more
self-sufficient upbraided. Both were needlessly apprehensive of rivals, the man was
utterly theirs, but with his manhood filched
by circumstance.

There was, of course, at the same time
during the war much excessive sex stimulation and promiscuous intercourse. That
secured public attention. The reverse was
scarcely discussed. To a pair, unaware of the
type of man who went through such a strain of
the nerves as to amount to real injury without showing any other external sign of the
results of this strain except an incapacity to
play the physical part of a husband, this may
appear to be somewhat strange. Yet, beyond
doubt, one of the results of the war was to
reduce the sex potency of many fine types
of men.

I have had the confidences of many men
very distressed by such an experience. Each

has been chiefly distressed because he found
himself unable to convince his loving wife
that she was not in the least degree to blame;
that their own true love had not in the least
diminished; that there was no infidelity; no
attraction in any other quarter; but that he
was just incapable of sex union. Essentially
a war injury. It is paralleled in peace by
similar accidents—when motoring for instance—or the effects of times of stress and
pressure.

Few men in such circumstances consult an
experienced medical practitioner; and if they
do they are not sure of getting the help they
need. There are few medical practitioners
experienced enough in all the subtleties of
such a case to be really helpful. The tendency
of most men toward another male in this
predicament is to laugh or to be incredulous.
If a medical man who is consulted and is
convinced that something is amiss does not
quite know what to prescribe, he need not be
ashamed to be unable to advise successfully
regarding the cure, for such physiological
needs of mankind have been but little studied
or discussed, save by a few experts.

Of course, whenever there is obvious nerve
strain or deep injury, recovery is slow; much
time must elapse and very loving care must
be given in the home. The wife must be all

compounded of self-abnegation and sympathy, of bracing stimulation and good cheer if failure again results. One of the great difficulties after such an injury is the later psychic reactions, and in particular the nervous fear on the part of a man that he will fail again, even though he is supposed to be cured. His very anxiety to succeed unfortunately tends to react in the same direction as the original injury and to prolong the difficulties. So long as there is a strain, or the effects of injury are still apparent or the man is in any way below par, patience and the absence of all attempts at union is the proper course to follow When the *general* health is restored it is often advisable and legitimate to assist the sex glands to regain their proper balance by taking a short course of special glandular extracts. Read Appendix, p. 207, in this connection. For such needs probably those extracts recommended on p. 211 would be found most helpful for temporary use. Then when cure may be anticipated, the great desideratum is to restore to the man the necessary confidence in himself so that the expression of his passionate love may not be thwarted by the inhibiting effects of anxiety. Almost as dependent on her as a child, the man will need his wife's help. The wife must play a very difficult and very self-sacrificing part. However passionate her own desire may be, she must curb it and restrain it, and not allow any external sign of it to disturb the time of cure. When union is pronounced possible, she must woo and encourage her husband in many ways, and if he fails must smile the failure away with hopeful encouragement that the next time all will be well. Nothing has a greater physiological reaction on this experience in life than a sense of fear or discouragement.

The advice given on p. 48, Chapter III, should assist the woman to keep her own balance and normality while she is lovingly leading her husband through his difficult time back to full marital power. The restoration should react on the whole system and custom enhance the enriching and vivifying ritual.

Another type of reduced sex vigour in man, which inspires less sympathy perhaps, and is of a different origin, is that sometimes initiated by masturbation or "self-abuse." The number of men who suffer in this way, and thus cause their wives untellable suffering, is much greater than "scientific experts" generally imagine. There have been for centuries past innumerable outpourings of scorn, indignation and reproof about masturbation, and multitudinous warnings against it have been uttered. It appears to me they have usually been couched in terms of such extreme exaggeration as to be self-evidently untrue, or based upon arguments which are not convincing because they are not fundamentally right as to the reasons why that practice should be avoided. In recent years, some men (particularly schoolmasters) have shown a reverse tendency, and they not merely connive at masturbation in boys and young men, but condone it with what seems to me the effrontery of bravado. A few dare to claim that it is perfectly right and natural and even that masturbation is almost universal in boys and young men.

This appears to me to be an abominable libel on the majority of decent young Englishmen and the mothers who had brought them up and whose wisdom and loving counsel from their nursery days should have safeguarded them from the dangers of accustoming themselves to such a perversion.

While, on the one hand, the distorted fear of it and the exaggerated denouncements are quite misleading, this modern attitude is, in my opinion, almost equally harmful. Among the unhappy marriages one can trace the source of the rift in the lute to the fact that the man had no idea till *after* marriage what true sex union involved and how he was unfitting himself for it and thus risking his whole life's harmony by self-indulgence.

I want to emphasise this because there is one intensely important reason against the practice which I have never yet seen explicitly stated anywhere by anyone, even in the most elaborate treatises on the subject. This reason I will give briefly in the following paragraphs, but before doing so, I wish to make it clear that this does not apply to isolated or a very few infrequent uses of masturbation by healthy, normal young men or boys. I sometimes get letters and confidences from unmarried men who fear they will go mad, or dare not marry because they have committed the "mortal sin" once or twice. Priests have much to answer for by wicked exaggeration in condemning what is a real evil. Such men should be reassured. If there is no misrepresentation so that no unnaturally excessive repentance and fear is generated in the young man's mind, and if normal, healthy and strong in other ways, and he has only a few times in his life indulged in masturbation, he really need have no anxiety. The chances are remote indeed that any harm can have been done. I think it only fair to state this quite explicitly in view of the hectic absurdities which many preach to the young about this topic.

On the other hand, it is most improper that the young should not be warned of the *real* danger to their mature sex life involved in the practice. It is this:

The act of sex union is not a purely physical thing, but the physical machinery of sex union is set in motion by the mental thoughts, the sentiments, which stir the mind and heart of a human being. The nerve centres which are placed locally round the male organ, and the accessory structures are directly acted upon by the imagination—the sentiments which are experienced by the higher brain. On the other hand, the purely physical accumulations of glandular secretions and maturing spermatozoa in the ripe, active young male may also lead to the purely physical phenomenon of an erection. Again an erection may be acquired by the crude physical means of masturbation by friction. In all these ways the erection and the nerve stimulus lead to the intense nervous crisis of an orgasm. But the quality, meaning and physical value of that orgasm differs according to the attendant circumstances. After the normal, wholesome reactions experienced by the lover in his act of true union, every nerve is soothed and refreshed by normal sleep and all the attendant circumstances of a wholesome and real sex union (see Chapter VIII, pp. 117 et seq.), including the subtle absorptions

F

from the complementary sex which are so important.

The masturbator on the other hand in order to obtain the gratification of the excitement of the orgasm, stimulates the *local* nerves in such a way as to bring on the crisis. This stimulation is throughout unnatural, and generally cruder, rougher and different from the local stimuli which are experienced in the true sex act. Without elaborating the differences in complete detail, the quality and type of these differences will be realised when it is appreciated that in the normal way the extremely sensitive tissues of the *glans penis* (at other times protected by its enveloping hood of skin) are in contact only with the very soft, moist and delicate tissues of the feminine vaginal walls. Thus the stimulation is most delicate, without friction or roughness, and gently leading up to the crisis, all the while the sensitive tissues are being protected as Nature intended by the natural moisture and the soft delicate skin of the organs, with which they alone are supposed to come in contact. By the cruder methods of masturbation, the sensitiveness of the reaction is reduced and the glans accustomed to a friction and contact different from that it is intended to experience.

Of course in this matter, there is immense

individual variability, and many men appear to have masturbated with impunity, but the general tendency of masturbation is to accustom the reaction to a harsher and cruder type of stimulus than Nature arranges. Also an unnatural position is adopted, which tends to coarsen, intensify, or at any rate alter the degree of stimulation necessary to consummate the orgasm. The thoughts and mental pictures too, must of necessity be removed from the true object of a man's affection. Masturbation does not necessarily reduce sex-vigour in men, but it often diverts it from its proper channels, and it is to be avoided wherever possible. In matters concerning sex stimulation, more intensely even than in other functions, physiological processes quickly take on habits. A young man who has indulged in masturbation for years may find that when he marries, however much he may love his wife, the natural stimulus afforded, the delicate local friction arranged by Nature for the mutual act of union for himself with his wife do not result in the type of stimulation to which his sex organs have unnaturally accommodated themselves. He may then find, what many unfortunate men have found after marriage, that the normal stimulus of normal union does *not* suffice to bring on the natural crisis of orgasm. When this is so, there may be serious rocks ahead in the marriage.

It is extremely difficult to give to young men and boys even an outline of all that this involves, but I feel that it is one of the urgent necessities of the day that this should be done, and they should at least partly understand why it is folly to acquire the habit of masturbation. Far too often it is the public schoolboy who drifts or is encouraged to enter into a practice such as this, which may jeopardise the ultimate and lasting success of his true marriage by warping and altering the orientation of the intricate and sensitive instrument with which he should later bring his marriage to its physical perfection.

An example of this is seen in Mr. C., who is 31 and describes himself "as strong as a horse," weighs 11 stone and is 5.10 in height. But his nervous system is "all to pieces" and he suffers from fits of profound depression, and in the sex act itself attains only the preliminaries with a fleeting erection which renders it impossible for him to perform the normal sex union. He traces this to masturbation continued since his school-days.

The present social and economic conditions leading to late marriage in the professional and upper classes result in many women having to face the problem of a husband in whom some such characteristic has been developed in a greater or less degree. What then can be done?

If, as is very likely, the man truly loves his wife, and is acutely distressed to find himself more or less incapable of playing his part in marriage as it should be, he probably will be only too eager to do anything which can be done to set matters right. Alas, I have no easy cure to offer. The wife will require intense patience in the encouragement of her husband. She should endeavour to try a considerable variety of positions, as sometimes adjustment is difficult one way but quite easy and happy in another (see also p. 147).

Sometimes young people consult me because they have been told that masturbation causes insanity in their children. They should be reassured. They should pay no attention to this idea, as it is fantastic nonsense.

Many healthy men who have masturbated become perfectly normal husbands: more would do so if it were not for the *fear* of madness or some dire consequence of masturbation which has been inculcated in them by a "religious revival" preacher or by some of the hectic books widely distributed. The very *fears* they entertain have physical reactions of a depressing nature on the whole metabolism. Also fear acts directly on the nerves controlling the localised blood supply which should create the erection without which the penetration of normal union cannot be effected. Self-confidence is the secret of successful sex-life in the male.

The type of impotence which a really normal man nevertheless suffers from, due to the inhibitions of *fear*, I call "phantasmal-impotence." It is easy enough to cure in an hour if the real confidence and understanding of the man are gained and he is made to realise that the exaggerated nonsense he had been told was the cause of the fear he feels, and that the fear itself caused the impotence. Once the fear is removed the man may enjoy normal coitus thereafter.

A sense of *guilt* acts in the same way as does fear in creating phantasmal-impotence. Inculcated in early youth, an excessively puritanical attitude, coupled with prudery, is still to be found in some homes where a false interpretation of Christianity has smothered the normal sex instincts and befouled the dignity of sex life with the perverted idea that it is base. This attitude of mind is more often permanent in women than in men, yet it still exists in some men and acts as a bar to normal health in marriage.

The very antithesis of the masturbator is

he who has refrained absolutely from *all* manifestations of sex and led a life of complete repression. This type of man is he who has been brought up to maintain his own "purity" by keeping entirely apart from women till he is well over thirty or even forty. At forty perhaps, when he may be in a position to marry, he falls in love, possibly all the more intensely because of the earlier repressions. But throughout the years of his "purity," he has not been able to avoid nocturnal pollutions. Those he has been encouraged to consider quite normal. And so they are for a *few* years while a young adolescent is growing into full manhood. It is *not* intended by Nature for a man of full age to continue unmarried year after year. Early marriage is the natural and still the right thing. Almost every day that passes increases my conviction that the race runs innumerable dangers from the habit of delaying marriage which is becoming so common. Late marriage is the source of innumerable physical and social evils and incalculable unhappiness and discontent. Nature may have her revenge, and on his late marriage a man may find himself impotent or nearly so, or else so excited and overwrought by union that a true marriage is almost or quite impossible, because of premature ejaculation (see p. 75). The best way to avoid such evils and to live normally is to marry *young* and to remain in love.

Dr. Arthur Cooper very truly said: "Everything depends on the individual, but probably it may be laid down as a general rule that enforced and protracted continence is almost always injurious to a less or greater extent, according to its duration." (*The Sexual Disabilities of Man*, London, 1920.)

As I have rather fully explained the value of nourishing the system with the complex molecules it lacks in certain conditions on pp. 46, 7, I ask those who have not read those pages now to do so, as I wish to consider here the application of extracts of certain glands to restore normality in men who suffer from such deficiencies as have just been described. It will not be surprising that a function so dependent on glandular activity as the male sex function should sometimes fail of perfect balance and thus benefit by supplementary glandular treatment. A number of different glands secreting in different parts of the body affect and control the male sex activities. If any one of these is deficient or excessive, and there is a lack of balance in the internal glands, some abnormality or difficulty in the normal sex life will be experienced. Where there is a deficiency in any one gland it soon affects the others as their action and reaction on each other is so closely connected. Hence for a general failure and lack of vitality pluri-glandular compounds of various sorts (that is mixtures of different extracts made up to suit the needs of individuals) are most likely to benefit those below par in one way or another. (See Appendix A, No. 2.)

Where there is no definite history of accident or injury to account for the loss of vitality, and the man is merely very much below normal, the administering of some glandular extract is most likely to lead to a favourable result. A suitable mixture persisted in would probably successfully restore the man's normal sex activity in two or three months. It may even overcome what may appear to be a state of incapacity to produce active spermatozoa, and thus restore fertility apparently lost.

The suggestions made in this chapter are based on the assumption that the man is married to a normal woman and suffers from and is conscious of his own deficiency, desiring to be restored to normal virility. There are, however, men who *think* themselves below normal, are even greatly worried by what they consider or their wives tell them is their semi-impotence, when all the

time they are fully normal but married to
wives who are exceptionally highly sexed.
The chapter on *frequency* (p. 127) will throw
some light on this problem. A man must be
careful not to underestimate his own degree
of normality and strength, for I have had
confidences from some men, who, married
to over-sexed women, felt themselves partially
impotent because they could "only" indulge in
sex union once a day! This is not only amply
"normal" but in excess of what I should
consider a perfectly natural amount of sex
experience if it be continued over years. Any
man who finds himself in this position should
not feel any personal self-reproach and should
not endeavour in any way to increase his
potency but should advise his wife to follow
the suggestions made in Chapter III, p. 48.

Chapter V

Premature Ejaculation

"Incontinence in love is surely this
To spill the nectar that should rise to bliss."
                                                    ANON.

IT should first be explained that by "Premature Ejaculation," I do not mean the ordinary haste and carelessness used by all too many quite normal men in the marital act, and discussed in *Married Love*. There I offered help and instruction to healthy young men and women. Now in this chapter I refer to slight departures from the normal. These consist mainly in explosive or immediate ejaculations so that even the man's own reactions are incomplete. Ejaculation may be so hasty that the first touch, the contact even of the limbs, is sufficient to cause the discharge of the seminal fluid externally, or it may be that a few seconds only elapse so that for the man an incomplete orgasm follows immediately on insertion. The former extreme condition results in virtual impotence if it is a habit, as it renders the man incapable of union. On the other hand, if it only occurs, as it does so often, at the commencement of marriage, it may be overcome by the man but leaves disastrous and lasting consequences on the woman (see Chapter VI, p. 97).

The more usual degree of *ejaculatio præcox*, as it is technically called, permits of entry and some degree of orgasm to the man, but deprives him as well as his wife of complete and satisfying reactions.

The wide prevalence of premature ejaculation in British men of the professional and upper classes has surprised me. I have little evidence of its existence as a "problem" in the homes of the manual workers, and incline to think it much rarer there than among the "black coated." Among Public School and University men it is one of the marital difficulties oftenest brought to my notice. I know, not only that a large number of men suffer in this way, but that they are often the very men who would never be suspected of any lack of normal sex capacity even by their medical attendants. A practitioner may be treating the man's wife for "nerves," "neurasthenia," "chlorosis," or other and more serious diseases, without the smallest clue as to what is really wrong.

Marital failure due to this cause may often lead to a chain of evils—ill-health, bad temper, divorce, forming a natural sequence where some sufficiently strong counter-balancing factor is absent.

I have had a good many confidences from men who have read and followed the advice given in *Married Love* so far as they can when handicapped by this personal weakness, and who find so long as they suffer from it that it is generally impossible to secure that complete sex-reaction which alone entirely and completely satisfies both of the married pair.

The case of Mr. H. is typical of that of far too many men: "I am a married man of 27 with one charming baby. When I married (two years ago) I found that the act of union with my beloved wife gave me very little *physical* pleasure, and also that ejaculation took place almost as soon as union had been effected. This latter has been a constant source of sorrow to me, for it has meant that I have never been able to continue coitus long enough to give my beloved her orgasm. My will has no power whatever over the action. Try as I may I cannot keep back the ejaculation for more than a minute or so, and this only by keeping perfectly still. If I excite the penis by movement, my orgasm

takes place in much less time. Since marriage
we have had relations on an average once in
four or five days with longer breaks at times."

He asks: "Can anything be done besides
the effect of abstinence for a long time to
delay the completion of the sex act on my
part? Is any medical treatment possible? I
would willingly do anything to become normal
in this respect."

Mr. H.'s reactions were complicated by
the fact that for many years he had been
the slave of the habit of masturbation, some
of the effects of which are curiously liable
to act in opposite directions with different
types of men. That is to say that the excessive
masturbator, when he does at last love and
marry, may find himself suffering from such
hasty ejaculations that he cannot experience
quite normal coitus with his wife. On the
other hand, he may find the reverse, and be
distressed by the fact that the natural
stimulus of union is insufficient to cause an
orgasm at all, and he has too long protracted
erections with a loss of capacity to ejaculate.

At present, let us consider the sufferer from
hasty ejaculation—what can he do? Mr. H.
(as quoted above) was under the impression
that long continued spells of abstinence
assisted towards a cure. This is a fairly
common error. Abstinence is useful, essential

for many other reasons, but is of little value as a contributory factor in curing premature ejaculation. On the contrary, one of the courses of procedure which I have often advised, and with some success, is that the sufferer should definitely endeavour to have a second union the very same night, or the very next night, after a union which has been spoilt by premature ejaculation. In cases not complicated by masturbation or prostatic enlargement long periods of repression and abstinence are sufficient in themselves to *cause* too-hasty ejaculation owing to the accumulations both of pent-up desire and actual secretions. Then normal coitus at more frequent intervals suffices to effect a complete cure.

Such a type of too-hasty ejaculation as this may arise in a marriage which has been hitherto well-adjusted as a result of a long illness of one of the pair, or a long spell of enforced separation. For them, natural unions, the exertion of will-power, and the exercise of common sense, suffice to cure the trouble.

But to return to such a case as that of Mr. H., who has for so long suffered from this humiliating defect that will-power proved of little assistance by itself: Is any further help available? Yes. I have considered the many factors involved in a number of such cases, and have come to the conclusion that an important factor may be the state of excessive sensitiveness of the epithelium covering the *glans penis*. This is sometimes coupled with a condition which arises as a result of a cured, or would-be cured masturbator fearing to touch himself locally and thus leaving the foreskin unretracted when, in reality, a daily retraction and washing would do it good.

Mr. S. enquires about another typical problem. He says: "You refer to the importance of the delay in the man's reaction until the wife is brought to a similar point. But how can this be effected? My own occurs in half a minute or less, and I am unable to see how, by will-power alone, a man can delay it. I have tried by various methods, such as passivity after entry and continuing the movement after ejaculation, to prolong the act of union as much as possible. These are not satisfactory and I should be very glad to hear if there is any *cure* for cases such as mine. I am not young—in the forties in fact. . . ."

Mr. H. and Mr. S. both typify numbers of men similarly placed. They, like many men who confide in me, had been to one or more medical practitioners, but had not derived the help they needed from their advice. The majority of medicals at present appear to advise only "a bottle of medicine to tone down the nerves." Each must be carefully investigated as an individual case, and there may be some who only need their nerves to be "toned down." But the treatment seems irrational to me, and certainly does not meet the needs of many. As I could neither find *any* helpful prescriptions or mode of treatment published in recognised medical treatises, nor advised even by those practitioners sympathetic to and desirous of helping those suffering from this condition, I set my mind to the problem and concluded that a simple process of simultaneously disinfecting, cleansing, and slightly hardening the over-sensitive epithelium of the *glans*, might be of assistance. For that purpose I devised a lotion, compounded of very safe and simple ingredients which is given below. Until medical practitioners take up the subject and publish something better, I offer the following advice to men whose ejaculations are uncontrollably hasty: Daily to retract the foreskin to the fullest extent and wash directly with soap and cold water, rinse and then dab on the special lotion with a little piece of cotton wool, and leaving the glans wet with the lotion, draw the foreskin gently over the glans again. The special lotion contains

G

ingredients purchasable at any chemist, and
I should advise the man to make it up for
himself as follows:—

LOTION FOR GLANS.

1 fluid oz. Listerine.
20 drops Tincture of Benzoin.
1 oz. Powdered Alum.
¼ oz. Boracic Acid Crystals.

Dissolve the Alum and Boracic Acid together in 8 oz.
of hot water. When cold add the fluid ounce of Listerine
and 20 drops of Benzoin and shake.

Shake the bottle before use, and apply cold and without
dilution.

The above lotion was the best I could
devise, and since the publication of this book
a number of men have tried it and found it
benefited them. Others find it has no effect
on them. I might improve or alter it if I
had a larger number of carefully recorded
experiences. Hence I shall be much obliged
if any who suffer from hasty ejaculation
and make use of my advice, will be so
kind as to write me fully about the result.
Some men have experienced benefit in two or
three days, some in a few weeks, and some
have taken several months to be restored.
Much depends on other factors, and also on
the degree of the will-power, perhaps of all
the most important contributory asset in a
cure. If a man has persisted for six months

without noticing any improvement, it would then probably be better to desist as it would appear that the treatment is not meeting his particular needs and longer use of the solution is not likely to improve matters though it may possibly do so.

A good general tonic is often advisable, such for instance as Fellows Syrup of Hypophosphites. This is one of the best tonics available of a purely chemical nature and can safely be taken by almost anyone.

In some men the foreskin is excessively long, and this may lead to a difficulty for which treatment by a solution is insufficient. Circumcision is then probably necessary, although in a general way I am not at all in favour of circumcision. (See *Sex and the Young* by Marie C. Stopes, Chap. IV.) The exposure of the *glans* by circumcision tends to toughen its skin and reduce its sensitiveness. In a man suffering from excessive sensitiveness this is desirable, but it is far from that in men of the reverse type. The wholesale circumcision of young children now beginning to be fashionable among Christians in English-speaking countries, seems to be deplorably mistaken and likely to lead to a good deal of unexpected disharmony later on.

The marital problems raised by the "civilisation disease" of premature ejaculation have never yet been properly and openly considered. The whole subject is ignored as a rule, save by a few profound thinkers such as the American, Dr. Robie, and even he gives no practical *physical* help to supplement the great mental effort required to conquer it. Hence, the above hints, though so simple and direct, have been of real assistance to many, though I should like to have more knowledge, so as to be able to help all such cases. The wives of men with this weakness are often partners in the sense of frustration and disappointment it causes.

The causes of premature ejaculation are numerous, and range from purely mental reactions, such as fear of the ability to succeed, anxiety caused by over-zeal, etc., through the weakening effects of overwork or worry or lack of leisure to calm the mind; to more physiological causes such as the after-effects of disease, and also of long-continued abstinence caused by unnatural ideas or ascetic repression. The after-effects of masturbation or *coitus interruptus* or *coitus reservatus* sometimes result in an automatic and undesired expression of the *external* ejaculation which formerly (e.g. when using *coitus interruptus* as a method of "self-control"!) it had been desired to suppress altogether or to achieve improperly.

In addition to these causes, some men have naturally an excessively thin-skinned and sensitive *glans*. This is true of men who have been too radically circumcised. These sometimes find relief and a soothing of the irritation by the continued use of boracic vaseline as a coating over the *glans*, kept in place by a thin rubber tip-sheath. It must not be forgotten that in older men sometimes prostatic enlargement may arise, and this tends to lead to hasty ejaculation in some men who have hitherto been strong in controlling and timing their orgasms.

It will be apparent that to effect a cure of the husband's premature ejaculation, it is also necessary to ascertain the cause of the accompanying mental conditions, and then follow different methods of argument in accordance with the previous history and mental attitude of the husband. The co-operation of the wife is often required, especially where she is the one who has led to an excessive tension of repression by that one-sided demand for very infrequent union made by some foolish women for various insufficient reasons.

Chapter VI

The Frigid Wife

"We are sterile for lack of repose, far more than from lack of work. The wise man acquires wisdom during the time of his repose."

THE frigid wife is an artificial creation of unnatural circumstances. While in Nature, there must always be accidental varieties of every kind, the mal-adjusted do not increase.

Frigid females cannot be numerous in Nature for they are disadvantageous to themselves and to the race. But in the artificial civilisations proliferating for many centuries, the "frigid wife" (or the supposedly frigid wife) has been created wholesale to meet the unnatural conditions imposed on human life by the artificial falsities of society. In the past there have been more men of the type quoted on p. 5, who looks upon a wife in no way as a true partner in all things and a sex *mate*, but as a housekeeper and a breeding machine. While mankind was struggling to found some sort of civilisation, the dominance of the fighting male and the placid security of the home were undoubtedly very important factors in the establishment of security for the community. But these comparatively primitive phases pass: the false teaching about sex which they initiated remains. The result is that even still very many girls are brought up in such an atmosphere of sex repression as materially to injure and warp their natural development.

Some women earn the epithet "frigid" as a result of the artificial civilised life city dwellers are forced to lead. These are a special and, to me, particularly interesting type of women described in the ancient Oriental literature as the most highly developed human type: she who is sensitive to a daily rhythm and who is desirous of, and makes the perfect partner in coital union only in the hours of daylight and sunlight. For this type there is little understanding in civilised modern countries. Few, I think, even know of her specific existence. Sometimes a sensitive and loving husband will discover that his wife is of this type, as did an interesting man who wrote to me from Canada that he had found out after some years of marriage from a very reticent wife that her natural up-

welling feeling for union only arose in the
daytime and had waned by the evening when
with ordinary people nowadays coitus would
be expected to take place. A large part of my
work for the last ten years has been the free-
ing of our sex life from the shadows of suppression and ignorance and foul-mindedness;
perhaps now the world may be ready for
me to go a step further (a step I myself was
ready to take ten years ago) and try to get
sex recognised as a thing of the sunlight and
not the murk.

The false teaching that a woman should
show and feel no spontaneous enjoyment in
sex life does still profoundly affect a number
of women, so that, after marriage, their
mental attitude and psychological reactions
are such that they do not overcome the
repugnance towards the physical side of sex
which has for so long been inculcated that it
has become almost a second instinct in them.
This may lead to a slowness or incompleteness
in reactions which may be very disastrous to
their own and their husband's health and
happiness.

I have known many such women and their
husbands. I think in particular of Mr. D.,
who, after he had been married twenty years
and was the father of two delightful young
people, told me on the eve of my own

marriage of the difficulties he had had in
wooing his wife from the absurdities in which
she had been reared. It had taken him three
or four years before he could gradually woo
her to permit even the first union with him
in marriage. The deep and intense love they
both felt for each other conquered in the
end, and made them perhaps one of the
happiest of married pairs that I have ever met.
Few men would be so gentle and so wise,
and even if they had the wish to re-create the
mind of their brides, they would scarcely
know how to set about such a psychologically
difficult and delicate task. I mention Mr. D.
to show that it can be done, and that all the
exquisite beauty of the D.'s married love,
which I saw at close quarters when staying
as a guest on several occasions in their home,
revealed how well worth the doing it was.
Few such women could hope to have such
luck as a husband so strong and so tender as
Mr. D., and so their chances of becoming
fixed in an induced "frigidity" are great as
things are at present, though in an ideal world
they would be restored to normality by love.

Another cause which sometimes tends to
make a wife so frigid that she not only does
not feel any response herself, but cannot even
imagine the nature of the excitement and
pleasure experienced by her husband in

union is a purely physical feature—a minor abnormality in structure which is reported to be prevalent in the Anglo-Saxon stock. This is the tendency of the *glans clitoridis* not to be fully developed, or to have adhesions of tissue, rendering it far less sensitive than is usual in "fully sexed" women. I have formed the opinion that much of the talk of "purity" and scorn for normal sex life on the part of certain types of "advanced" married women whose cry is "union for procreation only," is due to an absence of normal clitoris development in themselves. This renders them incapable of experiencing and hence of understanding a complete sex life unless they happen to have strongly developed and quickly reacting *cervical* sensitiveness, which in some women compensates for the outer insensitiveness.

In my opinion the majority of supposedly frigid and under-sexed women could be restored to normal health and joy if they were sufficiently studied and their personal equation considered. The husband's attitude is of prime importance, but even his tenderest wooing cannot avail if the mechanism is rendered faulty by the wife's general debility or lack of co-ordinated function. Then he would be greatly aided by a good tonic or a suitable series of glandular extracts to restore the wife's glandular balance. True wooing and tender understanding on the part of their husbands is essential: without it love must wither, with it, when aided by knowledge, the "frigidity" of wives melts like snow in the sunshine. Dr. W. F. Robie, whose experience of marriage failures is vast indeed, has only come across two cases of incorrigibly and hopelessly frigid women. He says, contrary to the view so often expressed that a large proportion of women are frigid, that "a really cold and utterly unresponsive woman is a *rara avis.*"

The complexes of the nerves linking up the whole of the nervous system of the woman, and roused into action at the time of intense emotion, culminating in physical union, have two specially important localised centres, one of which is called the "clitoris." This is an external feature and lies anterior to the entrance to the vagina between the labia. Its position is such that it comes into direct contact with the base of the penis, and when the movement natural to the act takes place they mutually react. In a normal woman, this nervous complex is extremely responsive and is one of the main avenues leading to complete orgasm, but this may be under-developed in some women and in others may be almost entirely absent.

Where it is very much reduced or absent, the chances of the woman being able to experience the full nervous reaction of married union is very materially reduced, because most men, foolishly, only take one position for coitus, and a very small clitoris may altogether escape contact in this position. Some women on the other hand experience orgasm mainly or solely from the stimulus of the region of the cervix (the neck of the womb, an organ entirely internal), and never experience a clitoris-orgasm at all.

These two quite distinct sensitive areas in women, both of which or either of which without the co-operation of the other may lead to a full and satisfying muscular orgasm in women, give rise to orgasms differing both in quality and result.

So far as I am aware, the subject has never been considered, even by sexologists, as it deserves. It is extremely easy for an expert to recognise the physical existence of such a condition at a glance. Yet I only know of one paper, by an American, recording the lack of development of the clitoris in women, and these records were not correlated with the social results of the feature.

Interesting cases of the converse, that is of women with the clitoris unusually large, found it a great source of incitement to sex desire. Far too many marriages depend on the external clitoris-orgasm alone for the woman. This would be rectified to a great extent were men more cultivated in self-control so as to secure the cervical-orgasm for their partners.

As things are I am a little inclined to think that the supposedly "under-sexed" type of woman will be found to lack normal clitoris development. Her type, at any rate, is far from rare in our over-civilised stock. Such a lack of normal development is one of the profound physiological causes of marital unhappiness and disharmony, and may be the source of the real prude as distinct from the hypocritical prude. The latter is a normal woman pretending to be prudish, but really lascivious-minded, and using prudery as a cloak. The really cold prude is a common type, and is probably responsible for a considerable proportion of the one-child families, and of those who demand that sex union shall be "for procreation only." Knowing neither benefit nor joy in union themselves by the absence in their own structure of the key which would unlock their understanding to what a man experiences, they think of sex only in the terms of the resulting child. Hence after the necessary unions to create the child or children which they permit, they refuse to participate further in an act which to them has, and can have, no real meaning. Then when they yield to what they call their husband's "importunities" they are quite passive and frigid.

Then it is the husband's duty and privilege to study and explore delicately and sensitively his wife's nature, and do what he can to make up to her for the absence of the more easily stimulated centre.

Another source of partial or complete frigidity in a wife is fortunately more easy to deal with and can be overcome by suitable care. This is caused by debility and lack of vitality—what may be described as being generally "run-down"—either due to the exhaustion of child-birth, some serious illness, the conditions of strain in modern life, or what is often known as "anæmia" in various forms. For such women the best cure where the circumstances allow is to combine a rich, wholesome diet, a good iron tonic, and a visit to a bracing, sunshiny, vitalising locality such as the Swiss Mountains in winter.

Another minor, nevertheless unfortunately prevalent cause of disinclination for normal union, amounting to almost "frigidity," is caused by leucorrhœa (commonly called "the

Whites") and the improper treatment which is so often advised and followed out by sufferers from this minor ailment.

As there is some popular confusion between "the Whites" caused by that deadly venereal disease gonorrhœa and the simple catarrh leucorrhœa, I should point out that if even apparently mild "Whites" *persist*, a medical practitioner should be consulted in case venereal infection is present unsuspected. What I say in the following pages refers solely to the mild internal "cold" causing a slight discharge.

The simple form of leucorrhœa, which worries so many women from time to time, is debilitating, and is generally the result of being "below par" or "run down," and thus sensitive to "chills" in the internal sex organs, resulting in a local colourless discharge roughly comparable with the running of the nose. Continued douching is *most* harmful, and is, in my opinion, one of the chief causes of the complaint it is professedly used to cure. My objections to douching for contraceptive purposes have been fairly fully set out in my books *Wise Parenthood* and *Contraception*, but as douching is now so often advised simply as a daily "cleanly act," apart from contraception, I wish here emphatically to state that I think the douche, on the whole, is doing vastly more harm than it ever can do good.

It is positively pernicious when used as is advised in a widely advertised commercial "Advisory Bureau." Speaking of leucorrhœa or "Whites" they say it is "a symptom of vaginal catarrh," and yet in the same paragraph advise the use of hip-baths of *cold* salt water, and add "even after the leucorrhœa has disappeared a daily injection of cold or lukewarm water should be continued for a time." I regret to say that such dangerous advice is often followed.

In my opinion frequent douching is sufficient in itself to cause distaste for coitus. There are many reasons for this, some purely psychological. The "messing about" with parts which should be left alone as much as possible is one very obvious reason; then there are physiological, and I think also electrical effects in douching which act so as to disperse and destroy sex potentiality rather than build it up.

I know that many women allow the "trifling" ailment indicated by leucorrhœa to fritter away their strength for months and even years. They should take it in hand at once and *cure* it.

Ichthyol wool or Iodex tampons and an iron tonic are generally useful, but for this condition a woman should go to a doctor and demand treatment, and be sure that it is one which does not involve douching for more than a few days. It is best to confine the necessary douching to the morning.

If the husband's reactions are too hasty and he has either an external ejaculation at the very commencement of union or in the moment after entry so that the wife is neither roused nor satisfied, she is to a greater or less degree disappointed or disgusted. If the condition is long continued, it is very apt to lead to an induced frigidity in the wife, for what can she feel towards such acts of union save disgust? The mental and emotional states are, of course, of prime importance in controlling the physiological reaction in women more than in men. The "cure" for the wife's frigidity in such cases is the cure for the husband's condition. (See Chapter V. p. 81.)

That it is serious to leave things as they are is not only my opinion but is testified to in the following emphatic words of Dr. Robie, who says in his *The Art of Love* (Boston, 1921): "Ejaculation præcox . . . is extremely humiliating to the husband, and it is invariably injurious to the wife; for it leaves her without any normal sexual satisfaction, occurring as it does often times before her

H

desire is aroused at all, and always before she has attained an orgasm. She is thus left in a restless, unsatisfied, irritable state, which variously leads to insomnia, chronic bad temper, hysterical conditions, and other neuroses, as well as to frequent local physical disorders."

A special type of induced but lasting frigidity occurs in some wives who have suffered as brides from excessively hasty ejaculation on the part of the bridegroom on the wedding night or early during the honeymoon. Imagine the disgust, loathing and sense of uncleanness inevitably produced in an innocent girl, glowing with romantic imagery and sentiment, who opens her door to her bridegroom and in the first instant of the embrace merely finds the delicate fabrics of her garments suddenly soiled by a man who, in the same instant, is rendered incapable of playing a husband's part. How can she feel other than degraded and disgusted unless she already has vast patience, sympathy, understanding and considerable knowledge of the subtler problems of sexology? And even to-day few brides have that. A dozen and more years ago, when the majority of brides did not know anything about the anatomical structure and physiological reactions of their bridegrooms, the impression created on the sensitive and super-receptive mind of a bride in this unfortunate position was deep and lasting. A veritable "complex" was created which, as I know from several older married women who have suffered this and described their feelings to me, was as lasting as life itself. They became in that fleeting second of the husband's premature ejaculation, permanently "frigid" wives who at the best could but endure out of compassion or from a sense of duty the relation which should have been a joy. This, very often, is just as true even when the husband's failure was only a temporary one, due to his excessive eagerness and excessive desire to do right.

Mention should perhaps have been more explicitly made of this in *Married Love* as it was written specially for the guidance of young couples at the commencement of marriage, but *Married Love* was published ten years ago and had to be most cautiously planned to tell the really important *normal* things all young couples should know and at the same time to cause the very minimum of offence. Now, after the decade of open sex-discussion which it heralded, it is possible to be more explicit about some of the worries of people who are nearly normal but who in some respect may depart from perfection just enough to be miserable if left in the dark but who are so nearly normal that a little further enlightenment may help them to help themselves. Hence I advise any husband who, looking back on his honeymoon, remembers perhaps with burning shame, perhaps with surprise and irritation—such an experience in his own life, to study his wife's reactions to sex union since that time and if they are "cold" or in any way incomplete to endeavour to talk it all out with her fully and in detail. Even if ten, even if twenty years have elapsed this "complex" of disgust may be resolved and she may be at last given understanding and happiness.

Of course, throughout both this chapter and the last, I am considering only the condition of sub-normality in sex life on the part of one of the partners of a true love marriage. There is, however, naturally and rightly a repugnance, leading to an incurable frigidity, on the part of every normal woman towards any man she does not love, even if she has made the frightful mistake of marrying him. The prostitute type of woman can simulate and appear to overcome this repugnance by artificial acting, but the true and natural woman has an inherent and irrevocable frigidity towards any but her beloved.

Chapter VII

Aphrodisiacs? Rejuvenation? No!

"What should books teach but the art of living?"—
                                    DR. JOHNSON.

FROM before the time when ancient history runs back and loses itself in the tales and sagas handed on by word of mouth, is rooted the desire for a "love philtre."

Wherever one of the partners in love finds coldness or inability to meet the passion of the other, some stimulating aid to bring response is thought of at least, and probably sought. Mountains of gold must have been spent on efforts to obtain this precious yet elusive thing. How many witches, or those pretending to be witches, have been visited in the dead of night by lovers, seeking either to enhance their own powers of response, or to obtain some charm or magical philtre to give to the partner of their love or to the object of their desire?

With a snort of scornful superiority people nowadays read of these practices of old, but are there not in every city corresponding places? Shorn of the romantic accompaniments of cobwebs, black cats and dim lighting, yet surely we all know of spots where charlatans are performing the same function, receiving their heavy toll of gold. To-day they are called "Rubber Goods Shops" and under the cloak of semi-respectable business, they conduct a profiteering trade in trade-marked and other concoctions, under specific fancy names, recommended by some bogus inventor with false medical or false scientific degrees, professing to restore virility.

As came to light when the recently convicted Anglo-Catholic vicar (the Revd. Francis Bacon, alias Dr. Hannah Brown, alias Dr. Mary Lane, etc., see the daily press for the 21st February, 1928) had to face a charge in the criminal dock of selling drugs to procure abortion, he had also foisted reputed aphrodisiac drugs on the public with the pretence that they gave man the power to "re-enter Paradise for five shillings."

Whatever the trade-mark, the name or the pretensions of such drugs, pilules or decoctions, they may be generally classed as "aphrodisiacs." Some are for men, some profess the powers of a universal healer. Most of them of course are sheer swindles and can have no effect at all.

Who wants them legitimately? Surely many people. In some crises caused by illness and at other times by fatigue or strain, humanity does so sorely and so sadly hunger after peace following the accomplishment of what such things profess to do, yet cannot do.

In spite of the claim recently made by a Viennese Gynæcologist, Dr. Bauer (in a book translated into English by a medical admirer), that: "It is true that pharmacology knows of many means of increasing male potency and female desire; but these drugs, usually termed aphrodisiacs. . . ." Is this true? I do not know of one reliable trustworthy and really effective aphrodisiac drug. I wish I did. For I know of cases where it would certainly be invaluable for temporary use in helping to cure men who suffer from induced impotence due to fear and such other difficult psychological cases, which crop up with rather tragic frequency in modern civilisation.

I do not know of *one* real and really useful aphrodisiac. I know, of course, of concoctions which will appear to have some such effect for a short time, but it is an artificial and not a real effect, and it is followed by reactions which more than undo any good which may be done by the drug. The majority of the things sold, of course, are cheap substitutes, quite useless and merely a scandalous means of extracting money from the gullible public. Some are positively deleterious, and their after-effects harmful. In answer to the question: "Shall we, even as a temporary measure, use aphrodisiacs?" my answer is emphatically, "No!"

Can anything be done then for those couples where everything *seems* as though all should be right and yet it isn't? Where, for instance, the structures and organs appear normal, the health seems sound in the ordinary way, love is there, desire is there for union, perhaps involving a passionate desire for children, and yet partial or complete impotence, or complete absence of response blocks the way to united happiness and to the parenthood which is desired by the loving couple? Can anything be done for them? Yes, quite a lot can be done! By sound wholesome means, but not by commercial "aphrodisiacs."

Many factors must be considered, but in such circumstances as the above there may be some hindrance to the normal flow of necessary internal secretions. If then the system is supplemented by suitable pluri-glandular compounds not only will the general health and "tone" be improved but specific frigidity may pass and gradually give place to the normal desires for and success in union. This, in turn, reacts favourably on the health, and the system benefits from the union which in itself helps to restore the proper balance to the whole system. The return to normality thus assisted, it may be completely established and the health maintained permanently by the sufficient use of perfect unions. If no very specific indication of any particular deficiency is shown, I should advise a general mixture of glandular extracts in small dosage, for instance such a prescription as is in Appendix A, No. 3.

Probably to show a satisfactory result not less than a hundred or so capsules should be taken and, according to the size, sensitiveness, and degree of need for them of the sufferer they should be taken one once a day or one two or three times a day. To procure a *lasting* benefit probably the treatment should be continued for two or three months. These will react favourably both on men and women, for one curious and interesting feature of these glands is that where frigidity or deficiency exists, either sex benefits by the administration of these glands. Where they are taken with the deliberate aim of increasing the fertility, I think it increases the chances of securing that end for *both* of the pair to take them. It is very difficult to assess how far the deficiency of one affects the other, and possibly valuable time may be saved if both are taking them simultaneously.

There are, also, special glands characteristic of the male sex and the administration of the extracts of these either by themselves or added to the capsules described above, may be specially required by men. Such substances as Spermin for instance are often of special value to the male, as is ovarian extract to the female.

The general chemical tonics such as glycero-phosphates of iron or calcium may be given at the same time with advantage where the sufferer's general health is below par.

It must always be remembered that normal sex vigour is dependent both on the general health and on the specific condition of the sex organs and all their associated internal glands in their secretions. *All* need to be in good working order to perform their parts successfully and as nature intends. Otherwise there is discord in what should be a pæan of joyful and harmonious music.

Special treatment to supplement local failures or temporary defects is always combined with advantage with sensible attention to the general conditions of health. Diet, sleep, exercise, all can hinder or help the whole.

General advice as regards these things is more or less the same for both sexes. What is good in restoring normal virility to a man is also good in restoring her vitality to a woman. I shall assume that all the ordinary laws of hygiene are known and understood by the man and woman desiring to restore their own sex life. I will assume also that there is nothing in the nature of the serious diseases which have as consequences distressing reactions on sex life, such as diabetes and gonorrhœa, and that the man and woman who desire to help themselves to be restored to vitality have average health in other ways.

In the first place eliminate indigestion and any foods which tend to induce indigestion and be sure to conquer constipation. Ensure a rich wholesome diet, including raw eggs, oysters and whitebait, as freely as the palate can enjoy them. Also eat oranges and grape fruit and be sparing of alcohol, although do not cut it off entirely. Take exercise out of doors and in the bright sunshine as much as possible. More and more scientific details are coming to light as a result of careful investigation to confirm the wise old-fashioned impression that sunshine is the health-giver.

The best aphrodisiac is bright sunshine in the mountain air; spend long days out of doors in healthful but not too exacting exercise.

Another aspect of this question should be considered, and that is the bearing it has on the fruitfulness of the couple. I have had the confidences of many couples, and have sometimes been able to help those who intensely desire parenthood, but for some reason or other (often very subtle and difficult to detect) have been unable to conceive a child.

Mr. and Mrs. K. afford an illustrative case. They had been married for two years and were very anxious indeed to have a baby. The woman appeared to be perfectly normal, as was also the man, who had been very strongly sexed when young. He ached for fatherhood and was able to perform the sex act with complete success—*apparently*. I had the seminal fluid tested by an expert, and it was found that, although the spermatozoa were there and were normally formed, they were not vital but lethargic or practically dead. This, of course, was a fully sufficient reason to account for the wife's lack of conception. As I presumed that no single gland in particular was lacking in this perfectly balanced healthy young couple, I suggested to them to try a pluriglandular compound

(see also p. 207). In order to make doubly
sure, I advised *both* the wife and the husband
to take a moderate small dose of these daily.
At the end of three months the wife conceived, and at the proper time gave birth to
a very beautiful and healthy boy.

This, of course, is not a conclusive experiment. One ought to have tested the husband
alone with separate glandular compounds,
and then the wife alone with a series of
single-glandular compound, and had three or
four exactly comparable couples doing the
thing in different ways! But there isn't *time*
for that when people want a baby after waiting
for years! The fact remains, however, that
after a few months taking of the compound
extracts, the spermatozoa when examined
were fully motile, and the couple became the
happy parents of a beautiful and healthy
child.

And either directly through my care and
advice, or indirectly through friends, Con-
tinental and other medical practitioners,
and in various ways, I have heard of a very
large number of similar cases. So many,
that for *mysterious* sterility when children are
desired and no disease is or has been present,
I should now unhesitatingly recommend a
special pluriglandular compound, even if
other local treatment was being pursued, so

as to be on the safe side and eliminate any needless waste of time. A woman who desires motherhood sometimes wastes precious years and very much money trying one treatment and one operation after another. I think particularly of one unfortunate rich woman who suffered the pain and discomfort of three successive operations—when all the time she was absolutely normal and her *husband's* semen was infertile! Pluriglandular treatment administered pleasantly to *him* would have saved her years of anguish.

This must not encourage every childless couple to think that all they need do is to take similar capsules. The circumstances of each case vary, but here was one in which there was just that lack of tone and balance in the masculine system—normally a perfect system, which had run down to some extent and which was restorable by pluriglandular compounds.

This it may be argued affords a real and scientific aphrodisiac. I would not wholly agree even if the word had not become soiled and horrible owing to the swindling bunkum which has surrounded it for so long. For such results as are obtained in this way do but bring the individual back to the perfect balance and natural health everyone should enjoy. The unnatural stimulation, the

Aphrodisiacs? Rejuvenation? No!

"whipping up of a dead horse" foolishly desired by some cannot be obtained in tnis way.

Perhaps it may not be out of place in this book, which deals with some of the difficulties frequently experienced in the later years of love and life, to say a word or two about those most pathetic figures, the middle aged or elderly gentlemen who sit about on chairs in Hyde Park and escape, by a miracle, police-court convictions. The air of the Park does not act as an aphrodisiac, but the novelty of companion and the danger, some- times do.

When a man's friends discover that he is doing that sort of thing, they should quietly but firmly take him to an experienced surgeon, and have the necessary operation done promptly if there is found to be the prostatic enlargement one may well suspect. The sooner the operation is done the better if it has to be done at all, for the state of un- natural sex excitation caused by the unwhole- some enlargement may lead to incidents very distressing to the man's family. It is really so simple to cure him and restore him to the wife who probably still loves him and the family who feel a deep affection for him but have got into the way of smiling at his adventures. He is quite often a loving husband and father unaware what a lack of balance of his internal secretions is doing to him.

If this, the commonest and most likely physical cause of such ebullitions, is not present, the next most likely explanation is that the man has perverted and somewhat abnormal appetites. Never having known true love perhaps, or having wasted it in his youth by misunderstanding and the follies of ignorance, he now possesses only an acquired taste for what is false and meretricious in lust, and can get more nearly a thrill of excitement from playing suggestively with a *demi-vierge* than by any belated effort to crave the pardoning shelter of the folded wings of true love.

Ugly, obscene, their but half shrouded lives cannot be considered here. They seem to me pre-eminently the people to whom our religious zealots should address their homilies on sex.

There is another, allied theme which is much discussed at present—*Rejuvenation*. The leading surgeons of the two alternative schools are Voronoff and his "Monkey gland" grafts, and Steinach with his ligatures of the spermatic cord. Both these leaders have schools of medical followers as well as opponents. To discuss the subject of rejuvena-

tion would take us into the realms of surgical
detail far from the main themes of this book.

I cannot imagine *any* circumstances in
which I should advise Voronoff's operation.
For a few, Steinach's operation may be useful
but for another purpose and not for its
"rejuvenating" power, of which I am somewhat sceptical save as an evanescent phenomenon.

Chapter VIII

Post Coital Happiness

"If what I have written should give offence to any libidinous person, let him rather accuse his own turpitude than the words which I have been obliged to use to explain my thoughts upon the generation of man."

ST. AUGUSTINE.

IN *Married Love* I made plain *why* "The supreme law for husbands is: Remember that each act of union must be tenderly wooed for and won and that no union should ever take place unless the woman also desires it and is made physically ready for it," and that she is entitled to have an orgasm as well as her husband.

Since the day I enunciated it thousands of husbands have obeyed this law and thousands have been enchanted with the result. But all are not young, fresh, unfrayed by circumstance. With the passing of the years the first easily achieved glow may somewhat fade. Even married lovers may experience, with infinite pain and regret, the truth in their own lives of the old phrase "post coitum omne triste." Hence I feel that now I must be frankly explicit about another point in the conduct of the marital act not made sufficiently plain in the earlier book. It was passed over because I did not then realise so fully as I do now its intense importance, and partly because it seemed then to me the obvious sequel which *lovers* would not fail to follow. I did not then realise as fully as I do now how rare is an instinctive knowledge of the laws of love.

What I had to say in *Married Love* (see particularly Chapter V) mainly concerned the preliminaries of union: what I have to say in this chapter mainly concerns the conclusion and immediate after-reactions. I am now convinced that both phases are equally, though so differently, important.

Dr. Robie in *Sex and Life* says: "Does the bridegroom come forth from his chamber like a strong man to run a race? No. Ye Gods! He comes forth many times like the roué from the harlot, with a sneaking, hang-dog look, and with the inner consciousness that he has insulted, demeaned, raped a pure woman, and that pure woman the one in all the world that his flesh and spirit would ever cleave to."

However hoary the tradition, however many wise people have been misled, however universal the common belief that *post coitum omne triste*, I am convinced that there is a real message of abundant hope and joy for humanity in the revelation of the actual facts lying behind some really lastingly happy marriages which have escaped that feeling entirely. Perhaps, in the first instance they escaped it by mere good luck. Yet the luck lay in possessing a sound instinct. In my opinion, they have unconsciously conformed to a natural law which has a universal application—a law, therefore, which it is of the utmost importance to humanity that they should know and obey.

To make clear the difference between marriage as it generally is even under favourable conditions, and those who obey this law with real and profound success, compare Mr. N. and Mr. O.

Mr. N. is married to a woman whom he loves and who shares his feeling, and he is in all outward things the perfect husband. They are mutually suited in every way, and the desire for union finds its fulfilment in the natural sex act. After the crisis of the mutual orgasm, the man and wife draw apart. Directly after the ejaculation the man feels that the union is over, his sex organ

shrinks and becomes soft and he draws
away at once from the woman. That is the
usual consequence of the orgasm. The
moments directly after the orgasm are of
very great importance, and, instead of following the *right* course, the man draws apart.
Although they may have the sense not to
disturb themselves to perform any of the
foolish acts suggested by too many birth-
controllers, or to return to that invention of
the devil—the twin bedstead, they *draw apart*
at once to sleep. The next morning, little
details of the household, of the breakfast
table, of the day's plans seem to irritate and
fret the man. There is no sense of mutual
attraction; he feels somewhat below par, and
the kiss of farewell to his wife is perhaps a
dutiful, regulation affair, instead of being one
of warm tenderness.

Compare this with Mr. and Mrs. O., who
have learned the secret of vitality directly
after coitus. The union in its first stage may
be identical with that of Mr. N., but one
may be sure that during the union the wife
did not fail to reveal to her husband her
delight in him and that they mutually led to
an ever increasing expression of passion till
the critical pinnacle of the orgasm broke like
the towering crest of a sun-sparkling wave.
Thereafter comes the time perhaps of *all* the

most significant and the most potent. It is
not only the love play and the mutual rousing
before the union which is vital; the time
immediately succeeding the orgasm is even
more so and is even less understood. The
hour directly *after* coitus, the hour com-
mencing at the moment of ejaculation, is one
recurrently fateful in the love-lives of the
partners. This hour, mishandled on myriads
of occasions, has done much to injure morality.
What *should* be done is so very easy, so very
simple that the reader may slip past the
sentences hardly realising their importance.
I ask your very special attention to the next
page.

When the throes of the actual orgasm are
concluded, Mr. O. does *not* draw apart from
her, but with the very small movement of
his elbow and shoulder necessary to give the
leverage, he turns a little on one side so that
his head and shoulders can just rest on a
second pillow placed there beforehand. They
remain with cheek touching cheek, shoulders
just supported so that each may breathe
freely, and with muscles below the chest at
rest and in direct contact with hers. The
male organ, scarcely yet retracted, is held
gently but firmly in its place within the
vagina by the muscles of the woman's
thighs. The pair are thus lying almost on

their sides, and the seminal fluid is enclosed in the vagina in which the penis lies so that *both* are in a position to absorb and benefit from all ejaculated secretions. Without separation they fall asleep thus entwined. Thus, not only do they fall into this sleep with the subconscious peace and harmony of the most intimate realisation of unity possible for any human being, but certain very subtle exchanges and interchanges have time to go on in the localised sex organs. Within the woman's vagina at this time, that is after she has herself experienced orgasm, and after the husband has ejaculated, there will be not only the seminal fluid and the various secretions of the accessory glands placed there by the man's ejaculation, but there will be the special fluids secreted or ejaculated from her own glands, alkaline in nature, altering its usual content from acid to alkaline, and containing substances of inestimable value, but which science has not yet troubled to analyse and discover in detail. In these, the sensitive, very absorbent skin of the *glans penis* of the man is bathed and immersed. I am certain that ultimately it will be proven that the man absorbs directly and beneficially through the *glans penis* something of the woman's secretions.

Ordinary regimented experiment on such

points is impossible. One can only deduce the nature of the subtler physiological reactions from their results on human subjects. We can deduce what has happened to Mr. O. by observing his later behaviour.

The first sleep may last an hour, or all the night. The man then wakes to find that the sex organ is now normally small and retracted, yet is held lovingly against the labia of his partner by the slight pressure of the mutual contact of their legs. He moves apart, either to his own room or remaining with her. The next morning he is observed to whistle and sing on his way to the bathroom; to be bright and happy, to have a gaiety and vitality which has not been robbed but added to. Perhaps one may describe it best as being rendered more secure—more like the happy, spontaneous gaiety of childhood than the eager and hectic excitement of a desirous man.

Mr. and Mrs. O. have observed this feature in themselves for ten years, and Mrs. O.'s records show that although her husband is always good-tempered, and his disposition happy, he almost never sings and whistles along the corridors in the early morning except the day or two after the act of union performed in this manner. The man looks very much younger than his age. He had gained in love as well as given. He had realised in his own life the truth that in marriage a man truly should gain that which he hath not as well as rid himself of that which he hath in superfluity.

Let us now consider the case of Mr. and Mrs. R. They have been married nearly forty years; the wife below the husband in mental status, is socially very far from being a credit to him, and all the circumstances are such as might easily lead to an unhappy marriage and a dissatisfied man. Mr. R., however, is privately, and in all his home life, an intensely happy man. He asks:—What does it matter whether he goes about with his wife or not; let her enjoy herself as she likes best; they are far too good friends to worry about the extraneous things of this world. After forty years, he is ardently her lover, and each expression of their love in union is performed in the manner described for Mr. O.

Take another case, that of Dr. X. He has been married for over thirty years to a woman whom the outside world thinks extremely plain and unattractive—a hard, uninteresting "bromide" of a woman, stout, elderly, dressing in the conventional ugly manner characteristic of discreet matrons since Queen Victoria's time. To listen to Dr. X. talking of her, one would think she was a radiant and glowing bride, and still, after all these years of

marriage, two or three nights every week,
his hands stretch out across the bed gently
to feel her bosom. If there is none of that
wonderful tactile response which is characteristic of that sensitive organ, he presses her
hand and they sleep. Generally there is a
response, and they unite and remain united
afterwards as does Mr. O. Dr. X. is up at
six the next morning singing like a lark with
amazing vitality and a capacity for work to
be envied by most younger men.

I choose Mr. R. and Dr. X. to supplement
the illustration given by Mr. O. because in
both their marriages the outward circumstances are such that an ordinary dreary or
openly unsatisfactory marriage might well
have resulted. They show the powerful result
of satisfaction in coital love which overcomes
material obstacles.

It may seem a very small thing this
wonderful secret, this law of union. It is not
small. For humanity it is more important
than any one of man's laws. I do quite soberly
suggest, if it were universally known and
practised, it would almost revolutionise
society by making the majority of marriages
lastingly happy and saving them from the
sagging reaction so common in the hours and
days directly following union. It may seem,
perhaps, at first glance, scarcely of sufficient

importance to justify the immense stress I lay upon it. I want you to consider, therefore, what it really involves. They remain together. Instead of the separation immediately following the act of union, which usually truncates the experience after the man has parted with his seminal secretions and severs him at once from his partner, before any return from her to him can have taken place. Remaining together and sleeping together for an hour or more after the mutual orgasm the man's extremely absorbent and sensitive epithelium is bathed by the fluids in the vagina, and it has the opportunity of absorbing, especially from the fluids secreted by the woman during her own orgasm, something from her in exchange for what has been given. In addition, on both descend the feelings of peace, fulfilment, harmony and mutual oneness brought by sleep in the united position.

The crux of the matter, you may say, is not *proved*. It has never been proven that the woman, in her orgasm, does ejaculate secretions. About this point, I can reassure you. It is a scientific fact that a healthy woman in the act of union, having had complete orgasm does emit definite alkaline secretions. This fact is not universally known as it should be, but it has been known to some for many centuries and is demonstrable.

The next link in the chain is the question: Can the man's epithelium, covering the *glans penis*, absorb at all? Why not? It would be most unnatural if it didn't, for it is one of the characteristics of epithelia to be absorbent.

The next link in the chain of argument is: Can the *glans penis* absorb those secretions which are in the woman's vagina? This, of course, cannot be directly answered at present by any known regimented scientific test available now. It must be answered by the observed facts of such cases as Mr. O. and Dr. X. and many others.

Physiological science always recognises that the only ultimate criterion of anything bearing on life is the effect on life itself. No experiment is as sensitive as a living organism in testing results.

Much extraordinarily interesting research could be done on human life were human beings not so extremely difficult as subjects of scientific observation and investigation.

In this connection I feel tempted to recall the phrase of a wise judge, who said: "Give your conclusions, but never your reasons. The chances are your conclusions are right, but that your reasons will be easily demolished."

About this subject not only my own experience and that of several of my friends, but the experience of quite a number of those who have confided their affairs to me confirms me in my certainty, and encourages me most emphatically to say *Mr. O.'s way is the right way to perform coitus* (see p. 117). If you desire to benefit to the full by the consequent vitality it gives, instead of suffering the reaction of depression, and if you desire a life-long, monogamic union, full of love, enduring passion and lasting happiness until, as Darby and Joan, your lives draw to a mutual close, do as Mr. O. does.

Humanity often knows "How" without knowing "Why" about other things. Take, for instance, the recent amazing invention of the "wireless." We know how to take a little crystal, put it in a box, attach wires and hear singing miles away. What on earth has the crystal to do with it? A professor from the last century might ask: How can it do these magical things? It is utterly unproven —ridiculous! It seems to me that the inventor can very well reply: "It is not my business to say '*Why*,' I only say it is so. I merely tell you that it does it! Try it for yourselves."

That is my reply in this connection. I have found out a law of love. *I think* it acts through mutual absorption. I think that the day will come when it will be scientifically proved.

But the "*Why*" it does react in this manner does not seem to me the essential point for immediate consideration. Coitus thus performed *does* have the action I describe! Try it and see!

Of course, I must preface this invitation by stating that coitus, to yield its harvest, must take place between two who love each other and are in harmony. A man cannot rape a woman and expect to get this result. To those who are in love, and who desire to remain in love, I say: To save yourselves the agelong reactions of disappointment, which if you pursue your lives on any other lines are almost inevitably your lot, follow this advice. You will be conforming to a law of love which is something almost as magical in its power in human marriage as the simple little crystal in its relation to the new human capacity of hearing at a distance. It may indeed be described as the magic crystal to give you love into eternity.

Chapter IX

Frequency

"The End of Learning's only to Persue
The ways of Truth within and out of view."

S. BUTLER.

FOR years past, one of the questions often put to me, and that unhesitatingly even in mixed meetings where thousands of men and women were in the hall together, has been—What should be the frequency of sex union between the married pair?

It will be recalled that I pointed out in *Married Love* a very important aspect of women's sex life, namely, the discovery which has proved so fruitful a suggestion to other investigators that, in the normal, vital, healthy woman there are two wave crests of spontaneous physiological desire in each twenty-eight-day month.

This discovery was amplified by observations on sex dreams published by Dr. Havelock Ellis (*Medical Review of Reviews*, February, 1919) of which he said that "it is remarkable that they should both confirm what we must regard as the two essential points in Dr. Stopes' teaching: (1) the regular existence in women of a menstrual wave of sexual desire, and (2) the occurrence in that wave of two crests. This seems to represent the most notable advance made during recent years in the knowledge of women's psycho-physiological life."

In his large new volume which has just appeared (*Studies*, Vol. VII, 1928) Dr. Havelock Ellis devotes one of its nine chapters to a further consideration of the subject, amplifying the theme with details of cases of his own and confirming my main discovery of the two wave crests.

In *Married Love* I suggested that the mutually happy pair would gain were they able to adjust themselves to some such rhythm, and have unions on days round about once a fortnight, although I recognised that this would by no means be of universal application.

Surprising data have been brought to my knowledge at first-hand and have greatly extended the range of variability which should be credited to the "normal." One of the first considerations in dealing with this

subject is the question—What is "normal"
in the average man of our time? To answer
this question with statistical correctness is
impossible, for no one in the world knows.
In my experience, one of the characteristic
qualities of men, as distinct from women, is
that, about these matters, *every* man, whatever his type, always considers *himself* as
representing the "normal" man. Incidentally
I may mention that almost every woman is
perfectly ready to consider herself as an
exception—very frequently she herself sug-
gests that she must be an exception. The man,
however, who looks upon his requirements
in these matters as anything but normal I
have yet to meet.

Hence the range of what man considers
normal in himself is immensely wide. I will
quote the two extreme ends of this chain,
both from examples known personally to me
in my own circle of friends. Both were men
whom everyone from an ordinary external
point of view would consider perfectly
normal. They were healthy, well-educated but
not excessively "high-brow," middle-class,
decent "average" men. One of these men
could not (I think still cannot) endure or
practise sex union more frequently than *once
in two years*. His wife was content with this
standard and he thought himself normal.

K

He knew that other men were more inclined to "indulge" themselves, but he considered that reprehensible on their part, and held that if only they took a "decent" attitude towards it, they would be like himself content and healthy with one sex union every second year.

The other type in contrast to this, the husband of one of my most intimate friends, required and obtained for all the years of his marriage, until he was killed in the air, sex union with his wife *three times every twenty-four hours for three hundred and sixty-five days every year*. On the one or two occasions when his wife's engagements prevented the midday union, he was nearly frantic and scarcely capable of human reason before nightfall. Satisfied by his wife he was a joyous, happy, and delightful companion, doing richly creative work and full of vitality and charm.

Had I chosen abnormal, hateful or diseased people as examples of the two extremes of what one might call the range of sex union, one might have cavilled at my picking out such "abnormalities," but I am dealing in this book with the kind of problems arising in the lives of normal, ordinary people and that is why I wish to reiterate and emphasise the fact that these men were *not* abnormal in any apparent respect. Each considered himself not only normal, but the perfect example of a happy married man. Both were looked upon by their friends as healthy, average and happily married men.

Consider what such a range means! Compare it with the solar spectrum, with its band of deep red colour at the one end and vivid violet at the other, both fading to invisible colours (with which we will not concern ourselves at the moment), each normal. Who would begin to say that red was a more normal colour than orange, blue or yellow? Who is there to say that once in two years is a more normal period for sex union than three times a day? In my opinion, neither are normal, both are exceptional. Yet both were perpetrated by healthy, *apparently* normal men of the educated class.

I can well visualise hurried exclamations of dissent from many of my readers, that the illustrations I have chosen are unique, impossible, unbearable! But only a few weeks ago, when I was lecturing to a large audience, I mentioned these two extremes in answer to the enquiry as to what was the range of human sex union. A middle-aged woman in the audience came up to me afterwards and said: "I am glad you mentioned three times a day; it is what my husband still insists on, and has been having for years though I find it is too much. He tells me I am under-sexed."

"I find it is too much!" That is the secret of many an unhappy home. What is normal and natural to one of the partners is either excessive or insufficient to the other—that is to say, their physiological needs differ. If there is real love, even considerable differences may be overcome. So adaptable is the human bodily machine that the two may grow into habits mutually harmonious. But if the differences of temperament are excessive—if, let us imagine, the man who wants union three times a day marries a woman whose natural frigidity would make her the perfect mate for the man who only wants union once every second year, then the pull of the difference is too great, and a mutual adjustment, a really satisfactory harmony for the physiological lives of the two, is hardly to be arrived at.

This most intimate subject is one about which almost nothing is known to scientists and medicals who write on sex. So far as I can find out the only record about this point is one used in a semi-popular book by Raymond Pearl called *The Biology of Population Growth*. That is the record of only 250 men and they were *all* sufferers from prostatic enlargement by the time they were asked to state from the memories of their youth, what degree of frequency for sex union they had had. The extreme limits as given by Pearl for these men lie between "Once a week, or oftener" and "Three times a day, or oftener." Of the latter there appear to have been only 1·4 per cent. of the cases. The personal type or mode of life of the cases is unrecorded, and one only knows that they suffered from prostatic trouble. The range I give (p. 129 *ante*) therefore, from a consideration of thousands of apparently *normal* people is a great extension of our knowledge of the sex life of average people of to-day.

Dr. W. F. Robie, whose sympathetic attitude has brought him a profound knowledge of actual experiences, says on this subject (*Sex and Life*, 1920, Boston): "In any given case or any given couple, intercourse ranging in frequency from once a day to once a month may be right and healthful. A general average for couples under thirty-five would be five or six times a week, between thirty-five and fifty-five two to four times a week, between fifty-five and seventy-five, once or twice a week."

Personally, I imagine the great majority of couples over sixty neither desire nor would benefit from union so often as twice a week regularly.

On weighing and considering the stories of all the countless marriages in the professional and upper classes confided to me, I have come to the conclusion that a very high proportion, say about 30 per cent. of modern men and women are not in harmony, due to the fact that the husband's sex potency is far in *excess* of that of the woman. But at the same time, and contrasting with this, approximately 30 per cent. of women suffer from being married to men whose virility is *below* their requirements, and who, therefore, starve and deprive their wives of that sex union which their systems require. A comparatively small number (15 or 20 per cent.) of marriages are happy on the lines that the husband and the wife are either by nature, or by their own endeavours and control, *adjusted* to each other to give a reasonable sufficiency, without excess, of the sex union which both need.

Then there are marriages in which sex union has been altogether eliminated as a factor either owing to unfaithfulness, to the excessive work, or the ascetic nature of the couple. Some find, after periods of mutual strength and enrichment, they can live without the physical act of union, deriving from each other all their natures require from the subtler mental, physical and spiritual radiations.

That many women suffer from the excessive demands of men will be readily accepted by almost everybody. A very experienced society woman said to me recently: "The average bride returns from her honeymoon worn out. The man never leaves her alone till she has become a physical wreck. Then he goes elsewhere." Another said: "I am utterly sick of matrimony. I can't be nice to my husband by look or deed that he doesn't at once pursue me. I used to love him and his companionship, but year by year I am learning to hate him. Companionship has evaporated into unrestrained lust. He has become an animal."

The dominance of the male has become one of the established ideas of our civilisation. It is one which flatters man and encourages him to think that his virility is exuberant. The idea therefore is given public expression through the man-owned newspaper press, the man-owned publishing firms, through masculine authors, playwrights and publicists.

The reverse state of affairs, although it may be just as prevalent in the same circles, is rarely spoken of, and then only whispered with bated breath. It is considered shocking and abnormal, because it is essentially a grievance of woman. By the false, ridiculous and ignorant attitude of convention it is taken by the majority to be a reflection on his supremacy and a criticism of man's self-appointed place in the universe.

The *under-sexed* man is no more abnormal than the over-sexed man, but while myriads of plays are allowed to depict grossly licentious vice, illegitimacy and fornication, my play dealing most delicately with an under-sexed man whose wife longed for a baby, is absolutely banned by the Lord Chamberlain and prohibited production (see *Vectia*: A Banned Play and a Preface on the Censorship, publ. Bale & Danielsson).

This attitude of mind is reflected even in our very language. For a man who is deprived of the use of his manhood, and all the physiological reactions this involves, a word exists in the English language to denote his state, i.e., "emasculated"; and there is an active verb "to emasculate." There is no equivalent in our language to denote the woman who is similarly deprived of her sex life. Verily, nothing has full existence till a word for it is known and used. The idea that a woman suffers similarly and can be similarly ill-treated scarce exists because it is wordless through the ages. I will coin a word for it and that is *defeminate*. The obvious word effeminate having for so long held an entirely different meaning, and *ex*feminate, a possible new word having, somehow, the wrong atmosphere. Just as a man is described as coming out of a long illness or an imprisonment "weakened and emasculated," so one might say of many a woman captive in the bad old style of marriage, that she had been "weakened and defeminated" in it.

How few have thought or spoken save indirectly and in whispers of the deprivations silently suffered by the wife whose life is turned into a problem by the man whose powers, perhaps through illness or hard work, are so reduced that his mate is starved. She, too, in a different way, is defeminated by protracted abstinence just as a man is emasculated by protracted abstinence. The attainment of a mutually satisfactory balance of adjustment may be rendered easier for many by the help offered in Chapters III and IV *ante*. Some couples however will be inherently incompatible.

Before leaving the subject of frequency, I should like to say a little more about the fundamental physiological bearing of rhythm, because that is very significant in dealing with the physical state of marriage. In Nature, the only very obvious human rhythm which is unescapable, which, by its universality, has the quality of being "natural," is the twenty-eight-day rhythm of woman. Writers of many learned treatises have theorised on its possible history, tracing it right back to our primitive ancestors washed up like little jellied atoms on the shore at the mercy of the rhythm of the Spring and Ebb Tides. Without discussing such pure hypotheses, one can recognise at once that this rhythm is a very fundamental thing in the life of woman. It is therefore of great moment to the human race. Is it to any degree shared by man? The general answer to this question would probably be a laugh and a contemptuous "Of course not!" But it is.

Dr. Havelock Ellis says: "Of recent years, many writers, especially alienists, have stated their conviction that sexual desire in man tends to be heightened at approximately monthly intervals, though they have not always been able to give definite evidence in support of their statements." (*Studies*, Vol. I.)

I have had the privilege of seeing the elaborate pulse-rate rhythm charts kept for 32 years by Dr. Frank Perrycoste, brief accounts of which have appeared in *Nature*, 1891, the *University Magazine*, 1898, the *Medical Review of Reviews*, 1919, and an appendix to Dr. Havelock Ellis' *Studies*. It certainly looks as if in man there is both a seasonal as well as a menstrual rhythm in such a fundamental physiological function as the heart-beat. As regards sex potency, I have no actual charts of men, but several very interesting cases have come to my knowledge of men really and deeply devoted to their wives, who have, either instinctively, or due to my teaching, followed the fortnightly curve of rhythm in their unions, and, after some years, circumstances having separated them from their wives for some time, they have detected distinct evidence of a fortnightly rhythm in themselves.

Throughout the history of recent centuries, although monogamy has been the nominal social standard of the community, it has been a monogamy of legal fictions, its significance mainly being to secure the direct family inheritance. It has not been physiologically real because of the co-existence with this legal monogamy of large numbers of prostitutes and mistresses. These, although they may be suppressed and never mentioned in society, have had the effect of destroying essential *physiological* monogamy, to say nothing of the spiritual harmony of monogamic marriage.

Woman's twenty-eight-day rhythm and the consequent fourteen-day rhythm of her poten-

tiality of desire is an unescapable and archaic
quality in her. May it not become natural,
is it already natural, that loving and faithful
husbands too should have a fortnightly
rhythm?

During the Great War some men in the
trenches discovered this for themselves and
wrote to me about it. Although the facts
collected are not very numerous, they are
highly suggestive and very interesting, and
are confirmed by civilian men in more
ordinary circumstances.

Mr. W. writes: "Now I myself have lived
much abroad alone in the woods away from
females, and for several years past I have
been surprised to notice that my 'desire' for
a female arose naturally and without stimulation at always regular periods. Invariably
once a month (for a day or two at a time)
and when I was not over tired twice a month.
Even before I knew of your books I came to
the conclusion that I had a fortnightly period
of desire and could not understand it."

Another case is that of a married man in
India who had to be separated from his wife
for long periods. He writes: "I am not
young—in the forties in fact—but I am a
strong healthy man and I find that every
fortnight or so I experience a very strong
sexual impulse which lasts for several days

and is extremely inconvenient. It interferes
with my night's rest—a very important
matter as the work in the rains is exacting—
and in other ways. Relief, at last, comes
usually in my sleep, but I may say that the
impulse is at times so strong that I am
strongly tempted to relieve myself artificially
and only a feeling of shame and the thought
of my wife prevents me. I both work hard
and play hard and eat and drink moderately,
so that I cannot accuse myself of living a life
which tends to over-stimulation of the sexual
appetites."

With these facts before us, it is not fantastic to play with the idea that the perfect
mates of normal women would be men whose
natural and spontaneous rhythm coincided
in effect with their own. If ever the world be
fortunate enough to be peopled by a humanity
in tune with the profound and rhythmic har-
monies, and sufficiently conscious to choose
rightly a mate whose wave crests tallied
with their own, many of the problems caused
by domestic tyranny and a large part of
public prostitution would vanish!

Another helpful though surprising fact of
which I have obtained some evidence is that
a pair may affect each other so profoundly
that, not only in the woman, but also in the
man, a rhythm may be *induced* which becomes

sufficiently ingrained to persist even in the physical absence of one of the pair.

It is true that such men are rare and both they and their wives may be looked upon as being exceptionally fortunate. Nevertheless, if in a world where ignorance, suspicion, and the gross mismanagement of sex have hitherto abounded, some exceptions have chanced upon so happy a solution of the mutual difficulties of sex, and have been so closely knit that they have modified each other's rhythms to make a mutual harmony, are not such exceptions of the greatest inspiration to others? Knowledge that human life can be so successfully managed may assist those still young enough to be plastic also to achieve a similar harmony in their married lives.

The new generation of men is waiting for a harmonious solution of life-tormenting difficulties, and the examples of even a small number of actual achievements may, like the first crystals in a super-saturated solution, set in motion the potential form of a myriad others.

Of course, in a marriage extending over many years, as time passes the sex potency of the pair naturally reduces and wanes with increasing age. Ultimately, even such comparative infrequency as a fortnightly rhythm might, as the years inevitably pass, become excessive for an aged pair. But their deep and real love will not wane, it grows as the needs of the bodies are satisfied and the love-expressions they have afforded are woven into the texture of the soul.

So far in this chapter I have been dealing with frequency of unions, but within each union there is another point to be considered, and that is the number of orgasms each partner experiences in a single union with the other. A man can very seldom expect to secure more than one orgasm in a union.

The highest number of unions with orgasms a man has confessed to me in a *single night* is eighteen; but this was on an exceptional occasion for an intense lover after a long period of absence from his beloved. Usually if the man experiences a second or further orgasm in one night it is after refreshing rest or sleep between the unions. Women differ in this respect and *can* experience several distinct orgasms in a single union, though I believe the majority only have one. Some women do not sleep after a single orgasm but require two or even three to complete what is physiologically for them a single union. The American, Dr. Robie, says: "Husbands should know that some of the highest types of wifehood and motherhood

require, for their completest pleasure and
continued health, two, three or more orgasms,
all perhaps within the period of half an
hour. No husband should fail to detect and
satisfy such a peculiarity, which is by no
means an abnormality in his wife."

I mention on the previous page the highest
number of unions with orgasms experienced
in a single night by a normal man, and perhaps
I should now mention that the highest number
of continued orgasms of which I have any
record in which the man and the woman
responded mutually is twelve unions in each
of the twenty-four hours, continuing over
ten days. The man in this case would, I
think, be generally recognised as being slightly
abnormal as well as very strongly sexed, but
the woman was apparently normal and able
to live for long continued periods with no
orgasms, yet responded with an orgasm on
each of the twelve times every day for ten
days. The mutual exchanges which take place
in the properly conducted active union have
the effect of physiological nutriment. Those
who feel no need for frequent unions as well
as those who have not the ability to consummate them should not abrogate to themselves
the right to designate those who do as inferior
to themselves in virtue. I do not mention
these cases of very high numbers of unions

to indicate that I think they should form models for anyone to aim at or emulate in any way, but as records of what exists in people showing no other sign of abnormality, and therefore which must be included in our horizon when we try to consider actual sex life to-day.

Another important aspect of coitus is the *duration* of the union. I have said something about prematurely truncated unions in Chapter V, and in *Married Love* had just a brief paragraph to indicate that if possible the climax should be mutual (*Married Love*, 20th ed., p. 69), adding only: "But even after a woman's dormant sex-feeling is aroused and all the complex reactions of her being have been set in motion, it may take as much as from ten to twenty minutes of actual physical union to consummate her feelings, while two or three minutes often completes the union for a man who is ignorant of the need to control his reactions." I wish now to amplify this, and to give some further assistance on this subject, for it is a corner stone in the intricate edifice of sex life, and one which has often and often proved a stumbling-block.

The slowness of reaction to union which is characteristic of a very high proportion of women of Anglo-Saxon stock causes anxiety in marriages otherwise happy. The number of

L

husbands who have distressfully confided to
me their sense of horrible guilt that they have
to use some degree of preliminary digital
excitation in addition to the conduct of active
union to secure complete orgasm to their
wives, is so great that some reassurance is
called for. When followed by complete
normal union with ejaculation no harm whatever is done by this perfectly natural and
instinctive act. Nature, indeed, has so con-
structed about 70 per cent. of Anglo-Saxon
women that it is essential. How perfectly
natural preliminary tactile contacts are, observation on the higher mammals in a wild state
will confirm. I trust that among my readers
at least no more psychological disturbances
will be allowed to arise in this connection.

Where the health and the reactions are all
fit and in good order, the decisive factor in
the *duration* of unions often proves to be
the *position* adopted. In England, at any rate,
far too generally no other position is thought
of than the obvious one of the man superimposed on the woman. But this is most
foolish and often is the cause of really serious
though subtle disharmonies. Men, who generally are the culprits by insisting on this
unimaginative position (often due to some
repercussion of the "dominant male" idea),
are themselves the chief losers of the enjoy-

ment they might gain in other ways, while women are the sufferers from the deprivations to which it subjects them. Stated briefly and quite clearly, the longer the union (within reason, so that exhaustion does not supervene) the more actual enjoyment there is for the man. If, as it should be, the union lasts until the woman as well as the man is ready for orgasm, the greater is the benefit to her health. Yet, as a rule, the position insisted on by the man truncates his own pleasure. Dr. R. S. is typical of many men, let him speak for himself: "You came down quite hard on us men for quitting too soon. I think the truth is that we would like to be in connection for hours, but most of us have little control of *time*. When we are superimposed the pressure is too severe and all we can do is to lose our senses. It was only when I had had years of failure that I learned how to succeed *on the side*. In this position I have known of many couples in which duration of communion, which had been two or three minutes, changed to the complete length of time desired by the woman. I know many such cases in which the woman has *several orgasms* before the final one. I have known of connection lasting by this method from one even to two whole hours."

Let us also consider the experience of

Captain S. who says: "I have heard that
there are medical men who say 'The normal
time for coitus is about three minutes'!
When I told an old and experienced doctor
that I had been united with my wife for
45 minutes by the clock when we both had
orgasms at exactly the same instant, he stared
in amazement. Satisfaction for the woman,
in nearly all cases, takes time. And that is
difficult if the man is over the woman. It is
not difficult if she is reclining and the man
kneels to her."

I have read versions of ancient Sanskrit
books giving the most elaborate accounts of
all possible positions and their special virtues,
but much of the "information" offered by
these books seems to be not only fantastic but
phantasmagoric. Nevertheless I have been told
by native Indian men themselves married,
that they are personally capable of protract-
ing the actual union for seven hours. I have no
means of testing the accuracy of this, and
record it only because it has been soberly
and seriously told me by an Indian medical
practitioner as being true and confirmed by
more than one as the practice in their own
lives.

I offer no comment on this, but think it
important to point out the immense range
of variability in the coital act. This being

so it does not seem unreasonable that any couple who find their own particular habits failing to give them full satisfaction, should try the experiences which have brought health, peace and contentment to others. Though I do not know of any British man who can either maintain or benefit from union continued for more than an hour before the orgasm is reached, there may possibly be some, and I should be rather inclined to hazard the guess that their marriages are happy ones. They should, at any rate, make ideal husbands for the very slowly roused type of woman who is so frequently left entirely unsatisfied in ordinary hurried union.

Chapter X

"The Change" in Women

"What custom wills in all things, should we do it
The dust on antique time would lie unswept
And mountainous error be too highly heapt
For truth to o'erpeer."

W. SHAKESPEARE.

IN every marriage, even the most successful, a certain amount of difficulty may arise due to that time of physiological adjustment called "The Change of Life" in women. How many mysterious warnings exist about this, and what uncertainty and apprehension are felt! What a cloud it has created, what a menace towering over every woman and her love.

For the woman whose health is not what it should be, or whose sex life has been abnormal in any way, the period of Change of Life may be one of considerable disturbance. I do not propose here to go into the physical disabilities so voluminously and frequently described by writers of "sex

books" for the "edification" (or intimidation)
of womankind. Almost every "sex writer"
seems to have contributed some chapter, or
volume, or more on the menopause, full of
warnings, advice and hygienic instruction.
If I knew of a really good, encouraging, level-
headed book I should advise my readers to
get it. I do not! The books and pamphlets
on the subject are legion, a barren and futile
legion, harrying the women in their homes
who have never been wise enough or sufficiently united to turn and rout them. Among
them limps the type of milk and water
encouragement telling women that if, from
their early girlhood, they did all the regulation things, such as wearing flat heels,
eating brown bread, bearing lots of children
and so on, they will have no trouble. There
rampages the more "intimate" type of book
which lists and describes with a greater or
less gusto, innumerable physiological troubles,
such as hot flushings, the formation of adipose
tissue and varicose veins, and innumerable
other ailments which the poor hypnotised
reader cannot fail to anticipate are her almost
inevitable doom.

I should like to clear all the rubbish away
and in a few sentences only advise women
who have reason to think that the Change
of Life is approaching to carry on exactly as

though it were not. This is not always possible, but the mind controls the body far more than people realise. A healthy attitude of mind is of the first importance at such times. Then if any particular bodily symptom troubles them at all, such as headache or indigestion, or they notice themselves getting fatter than they like, they should go straight to as up-to-date a medical practitioner as they can find, and ask him to prescribe the necessary glandular compounds to restore their internal glandular balance—that "harmony of the hormones" which may be somewhat disturbed by the concluding phases of the active life of the ovary. A mixture of Thyroid and Ovarian substance and some others generally prove to be the most useful (see Appendix A, No. 4), and may be enough to restore the internal balance and hence wonderfully to improve the appearance and health of a woman whose system is giving trouble at the time of disturbance.

As Blair Bell said long ago, when there is an insufficiency of ovarian activity, the consequent symptoms "can usually be effectually treated by replacing secretions that are deficient, or by antagonising those which are excessive." (*The Sex Complex*, 1916.)

As I have mentioned fat I should perhaps

be very explicit that I here mean the *excess* of fat which often comes about the time of the menopause. Any attempt to use thyroid or other medicines or diet to reduce the figure below the *natural* roundness is both silly and dangerous. I think it a grievous thing that so many beautiful young girls should be hypnotised by the unnatural pictures and fashion plates in such decadent journals as *Vogue* and its kind, to think a stark and straight even a skinny or snake-like line are "beautiful" or smart in women. Nature intends women to be graciously rounded however slender. Rounded contours are not only the right and eternally true standard for woman's beauty, but they are of deep racial significance. To adapt an old proverb, let us say, "Angular women and crowing hens are'na canny." If anyone tries to take thyroid or anything else to get rid of the natural curves due to her sex she is risking very fundamental disorders and will ultimately pay dearly for her folly. The use of glandular extracts is only to be advised to restore a lost balance of the internal glandular secretions; and this loss is most likely to occur and require rectification at the menopause.

The ovaries, like many other parts of our bodies, give rise to internal secretions or hormones, which, distributed almost universally through the system, play their part in the controlling balance of the whole organism. It is easy to understand that when the time comes for such important organs as the ovaries to draw to a close their externally active life as well as to reduce their internal activities, that unless the whole organism is perfectly adjusted to this change, there may be various and apparently irrelevant disturbances and upheavals. Nearly all of these can now be almost immediately controlled and restored to normal by the administration of the necessary internal secretions to hold the balance until the disturbing time of Change is over, and the new type of physiological activity established. Nature sees to this for the fortunate woman who still lives with her and in obedience to all her laws, but alas, "civilisation" has so reduced the number of perfectly healthy women that the majority of us need some help over the difficulties of readjustment to a new phase of existence.

Chronic headaches and the formation of adipose tissue are among the most frequent afflictions of a woman at or around the Menopause. Many women suffering from these do nothing sensible to relieve them, and do not even *hope* to escape them because their outlook has been rendered unhealthy and depressed by all the ignorant and ugly nonsense they have read or been told about the Menopause. But my message is one of *health*, of sanity, clear-headed and happy-hearted *control* of the physical aspects of life in the conscious service of the mind and spirit. For physical disabilities, some form of physical cure or corrective is generally required, but *which* to employ is only to be decided after undertaking a clear-headed and scientific investigation of the causes. Now let us consider these headaches and undesired fatness.

It is generally recognised, now that the "hormones" or internal secretions are being studied, that as the ovaries give up their special work of preparing ova for fertilisation, and, for this purpose, cast them out periodically, they also slow up with their continuous *internal* work of passing certain ovarian secretions into the blood stream to travel all over the body and assist in the balanced maintenance of all its parts. At the same time the thyroid gland gets out of gear also. The lack of the accustomed amounts of the ovarian and thyroid internal secretions allows the cells which cause the deposition of fat to get out of hand and take too much upon themselves. As science is showing more and more explicitly, the thyroid gives a supremely important controlling secretion to the whole system. Hence the intelligent woman at this time will see that her system is supplied with small doses of ovarian extract and thyroid gland extract at least (and any other complementary glandular extracts which may be indicated) in suitable amounts to keep the true balance. (See p. 209.) Since the scientific researches of professors of biological and physiological science have discovered this new knowledge, it has rapidly been extended and rendered easy for medical practitioners to apply, and is widely used and appreciated in most modern schools of medicine.

A minor result of the "Change of Life" in some women is the growth of hair on the face. This distresses women intensely. A correspondent writes to me about this, asking for my opinion and help: "Hair on the face is a nightmare to thousands of women. Has it *any* direct connection, as is popularly supposed, with the degeneration of the sex organs? Do treat this subject on first principles as I have never seen it alluded to in anything but quack advertisements. All doctors do is to tell their patients to try 'Electrolysis,' an expensive and by no means always successful means. One friend of mine was scarred for life *very* badly over the whole lower portion of the face by too strong a dose, given by a doctor."

I know that this letter does raise points of great interest to a large number of women, and I think it is true, as my correspondent says, that no reputable information is available. Hence I will try to deal with it on first principles as she asks.

It is known that neither man nor woman are "pure male" or "pure female," but both are essentially *human* and in each are the rudiments of the sex organs of both sexes. As the embryo develops the secretions of the internal glands even from the rudimentary sex organs are hourly pouring into the blood stream "hormones" which have controlling and formative influences on the whole bodily organism. Some of these glands encourage, some inhibit various formations. The comb of the cock, his crowing voice and attitude are what are called "secondary male characteristics"; as are, in man, the hairy chest, the beard, the gruff voice. In the hen and in the woman such developments are prevented by the secretions due to her femininity. In woman the principal sex organs are the ovaries, the womb and the breasts, and the ovarian and mammary secretions do seem to be largely, though not solely, responsible for her feminine softness and hairlessness. Women, for instance, with malformed or deficient ovaries have been often noted to have incipient and even quite definite moustaches and other hair in excess of the usual womanly facial down.

Hence, at the Menopause, when the active part of the work of the ovaries is finished, though they remain and continue to give out secretions, they do not always do so in the sufficient amount to control the whole organism as they did formerly. This is true also of the mammary glands and others. Hence, the inhibition against forming masculine characters ceasing or weakening, they tend to develop. One result, which so distressed my correspondent (see p. 156), is the formation of coarse hair on the woman's face. An interesting confirmation of this is seen in the women who have had their ovaries removed. After the operation hair developed on the face; nowadays no reputable surgeon will remove the whole of a woman's ovaries if he can possibly avoid doing so. A similar effect temporarily arises in some women during pregnancy, when the ovarian secretions are inhibited, and they develop quite a lot of extra hair which simply falls off after lactation is concluded and the ovaries are normally at work again.

Now for my advice about this point to those at or approaching the Menopause. Do not wait for excessive hair to develop, at the first indication of coarsening hairs meet the enemy, not by defence, but by assault. Pull each out individually *yourself* (don't waste money on electrolysis) with special firm tweezers which will not merely cut it off at the base but will get it out deeply from the root. Merely to break hairs off coarsens and strengthens them, but to get them out whole by the roots weakens and sometimes seems to eradicate them entirely after a few months. At any rate the deeply pulled hair does not show itself at all again for about two weeks. This course, however, is only a minor preliminary to the main treatment which, logically following the idea given in the previous pages, is to keep the internal secretions going which inhibit the formation of hair. I should advise, therefore, daily small single doses of ovarian and mammary extract. (See Appendix A, No. 5). If taken in time and before the excessive hair had grown this would tend to delay or even prevent its appearance.

Women in whom hair has already developed should pursue the hairs also with their own tweezers as they show themselves again from time to time. Persistence in this course should greatly assist, if not entirely cure the

disfigurement. At any rate it is not only
more scientific but it is cheaper, *safer* and
pleasanter than electrolysis and other expensive treatments which foolish women are so
often persuaded to try and bitterly regret too
late that they did so.

To me it seems that the message to womanhood as a whole, to the mother, the working
woman, the thoughtful girl already dreading
"a full-blown maturity" is a very simple and
a very hopeful and happy one. It is this:
Almost all the ugliness, disease and dis-
ability you see about you, supposed to be
the inevitable lot of woman, *need not be*.

One of the cruellest, most senseless, and
at the same time very widely spread rumours
which is extensively believed, and has done
an incredible amount of harm in creating
unhappiness and upsetting the physical side
of marriage, is the monstrous idea that, after
the Change of Life has come and passed, a
woman must necessarily cease from sex
union with her husband, whatever his and
her own feelings may be! Educated and
instinctively sensible people may find it
difficult to believe that such a stupid idea
exists and dominates sane lives, but I have
found evidence that it does in many quarters.
I have found it believed so trustfully and
implicitly by such numbers of men and

women of all social stations that I think this
monstrous idea needs exposure and investigation. A confidence from a clergyman's
wife, herself an acute sufferer from her
husband's senseless decree against *all* union
after she had passed the Menopause, first
opened my eyes to the existence of this
barbaric silliness masquerading as "religious
virtue." In this particular instance it was
peculiarly hard on the wife who was one of
the "late maturing" type of women I have
described in my book *Radiant Motherhood*,
and she had not long properly benefited
from and enjoyed sex union before it was all
put an end to by the arbitrary husband who
would no longer unite with her on the
grounds that it was "against God's law"!
Although in his wife Nature herself was quite
obviously showing him that *Nature's* Law
was for him to fulfil his marital duties.

I have heard of quite young people grieving
that their happy unions would have to come
to an end when the Change of Life came,
and they would thereafter have to live side
by side but no longer united in love. In
some, perhaps foolishly, sensitive and "worrying" dispositions this idea of doom, the
arbitrary extinction of what they prized
before life is over, becomes almost an obses-
sion and haunts the happiness they should

M

have been experiencing unclouded by such thoughts. The husband who sighed to his wife, then in middle age, "To think it is only for a few years more that we can hope to be together. In a few years your Change must come and put a stop to all this," arouses my pity and my chivalrous rage on his behalf. *Who* told him the silly lie? I wonder how much immorality this cruel and false idea has generated!

Incredible as it may seem, this fantastic misrepresentation of physiological fact seems to be extremely widespread among religious people. I have not traced its origin. It looks as though it were one of the numerous by-products of the false idea, planted upon Christianity by the Early Christian Fathers, and still rampant, that sex life is a befouling thing only justified by the procreation of children. Even St. Paul did not go so far but said: "Defraud ye not one the other, except it be with consent for a time." Yet innumerable priestly individuals say explicitly and in so many words that "union for procreation *only*" is to be permitted.

No Church so far as I am aware has ever been so foolish as to make an authorised pronouncement of this monstrous misrepresentation, but it is at present undoubtedly encouraged by some of those in high office

For instance, the Bishop of Southwark, giving evidence before the National Birth-Rate Commission in 1915, said: "I have never been able to modify the view that the only thing that justifies ultimately the intercourse between the man and the woman is the purpose and the desire to have children." When he was then asked: "Must it cease after the possibility of birth of children? After the natural period of child-bearing must it cease?" he answered: "I should say so. I think that if you open the door to other motives, you are bound little by little to give the whole situation away." And to the Chairman, he replied: "I hold that if you relax the idea that intercourse has any other purpose ultimately behind it except the production of children, it seems to me that you open the door to a lowering of the whole idea of the union between the man and the woman, and you lower the whole idea of the intercourse itself." (*Report and Evidence of the National Birth-Rate Commission*, London, 1917, pp. 438–9.) Note his insistence on the word *lowering*, and the mistaken and narrow idea it involves, and compare this with what I have to say about true erogamic life and the *raising* of the sex relation by a truly scientific and idealistic attitude towards it.

It may seem a logical corollary of the

restricted theological attitude to maintain
that after the Change of Life, when union
cannot lead to child-bearing, thenceforth all
further unions should be prohibited, but the
whole of such a conception is based on false
teaching, which is alike ignorant of the logical
origin of sex union itself, of the physiological requirements of individuals, and of the
attendant benefits and enrichments of true
sex union throughout life.

Some elderly medical practitioners, whose
physiological teaching is tinged by "religion,"
are similar culprits in disseminating this false
and immoral doctrine; as for instance Dame
Mary Scharlieb, M.D., who even wrote:
"It is extremely pathetic to find women well
on to 50 years of age who are apparently as
keen on sexual enjoyment as a bride might
be." (*Change of Life—Its Difficulties and
Dangers*, by Dr. Mary Scharlieb, Scientific
Press, Ltd. [no date], see p. 35.) I refer to this
little book by name merely to be fair to its
author, and not by any means to recommend
its use, for its general hygiene seems to be
nearly as unwholesome as its sex teaching.
The author surprises one for instance by
saying that the majority need "some com-
fortably acting and efficient laxative" instead
of giving sound instruction that from infancy
onwards no healthy person need *ever* use

a laxative and to do so is to prove oneself incompetent in self-management and ignorant of dietetics.

Other medical practitioners have the outlook of the primitive "dominant male" with his open contempt for women's existence, save as a female animal. A typical example of this is seen in the publication *Woman*, by Dr. Bauer, a Viennese gynæcologist. The author bespatters his book with contemptuous sneers at woman, based on the crudities of a vulgar mind which concludes and agrees with Weininger's dictum that "Woman is only sexual." Hence for Dr. Bauer only the young and attractive woman exists—the others, "old maids," artists, social workers, home-builders, wise old women—all, that is, whose lives reveal thoughtfulness, work, and mental or spiritual charm, are to be snuffed out of consideration. He has no respect for age or experience, saying: "The mind of the old woman is as unattractive as her appearance." Men of his type seem to be incapable of seeing the exquisite beauty in the sweet and wise and tenderly loving face of one who has been a bride, a wife, a mother, who has nursed her babies at her breast and loved and served them, training spirits and bodies together to a fair and triumphant youth, and who has loved and grown with her mate

to the calm sweet wisdom of spiritual and
bodily maturity.

The opinions of crudely material and
base-minded men would not matter in the
least if it were not that they have for so long
been voluble and noisy and expressive in
print and thus tended to create a degraded
social outlook. It is true they are in the
minority in the medical profession, but
unfortunately the wiser ones have written so
little that they have not counteracted the
impression created by such widely dissemi-
nated writings as Dr. Bauer's, whose official
position as a gynæcologist appears to give
authoritative weight to his nonsense.

As one would expect, he can offer but little
help or comfort to women at the crisis of
the Menopause, saying: "The duration of
woman's active sexual life is limited. It lasts
only from the beginning of menstruation until
the menopause, and women know quite well
that after this their sex life is at an end . . .
but she does not necessarily lose her sexual
feelings and desires. On the contrary! . . .
may actually manifest an increase in sexual
feelings. . . . The woman realises the significance of the menopause and its cruel
consequences . . . that her attraction *for men*
will soon disappear." The rest of the context
implying that once a woman's attraction for

men is over her life is over and the body of
a live woman continuing to exist after this
time cumbereth the earth.

Two questions ask themselves immediately:
Is woman's sex attraction over with the
menopause? The answer, of course, is: No.
Some have no sex appeal as girls; some never
lose it. And why should a woman want to
attract *men* after she is a wife, a mother—
perhaps a grandmother? Is her own dear
one man not more than enough to fill her
days? As I have already shown, if the marriage
rites are rightly fulfilled, she and her lover-
husband are all in all to each other, more
deeply and truly one-flesh than ever bride
or unmarried lovers can be. The phase of
active sex-attraction for *men* is past as is
babyhood with its desire for rattles. Each
has fulfilled its purpose and developed into
the greater thing. The free maiden has
become part of the lasting union of an
enduring passion. It has built into the fabric
of the social community a stable, bi-valent
unit—a home-making, balanced, satisfied pair.
Has for this pair the joy and refreshment of
mutual union to cease after the menopause
has been grown through by the woman?
Nonsense! Of course not, and no one but
a theologian with a prudish, or a lascivious
medico with a dirty mind, and their misled

dupes would think it. Such exceptions in what are generally helpfully disposed professions do much to undermine the people's trust in them, and should be openly repudiated by the clear thinkers in both professions.

Incidentally, I might also counter Dr. Bauer's generalisations from an example of the type which might appeal to him: One of the notorious, beautiful yet naughtier ladies of high society of the last generation was commonly supposed to be so peculiarly popular among her high-class paramours *because* she had passed the menopause and was, therefore, able to indulge in more illicit amours than a potentially fertile mother. I remember my father, who met and admired her when she was elderly years ago, telling me that it was the talk of the men's clubs that this famous lady's menopause took place at the age of 27 and left her still for a whole generation sparkling with that "attraction for men" which Dr. Bauer says becomes extinct at the close of the menopause.

One has only to have the confidence of one's friends to know that the rich life of varied experience, the keen intellectual interests and the buoyant sense of youth which pervades humanity to-day find their natural culmination in a lasting sex-attraction of men and women for each other which rides like a gallant barque on the wave-crests of the various sex-crises, such as defloration, pregnancy, child-birth, to say nothing of the minor but repeated billows of menstrual tides, through the storm of the Menopause to the calmer, steadier, sunnier sea of the shores of the home land till they cast anchor in the harbour, secure in the possession of an indestructible love.

Contrast with Dr. Bauer's basely material attitude the nobler erogamic ideas expressed by America's famous psychologist, Prof. G. Stanley Hall: "Thus and thus only can the human male be given immunity from his polygamous instincts, by realising on how low a level his habitual satisfaction has been sought and how vastly higher and larger a gratification that is really sacramental can be . . . the charm of wives who can restrain and then wisely bring their spouse to a consummation that so compensates for in-frequency, is nearing the great goal and is giving wedded life its larger orbit. How the world needs again the wisdom of matrons, the counsel of Plato's wise senescent women, the need of which has long been felt but sometimes ignorantly branded as weird and even witch-like!" (*Morale, The Supreme Standard of Life and Conduct*, 1920, Appleton & Co.) And the even more beautiful conception given to the public earlier by Finot (*Problems of the Sexes*, 1913): "To maintain her charms, woman must first of all be allowed the ability to work and to act. Let us open the windows of her dwelling and permit the echoes of life to penetrate within. Then, instead of a half-dead being prematurely snatched from life, we shall find a creature of heart and reason . . . the ugliness of the prematurely aged woman will give place to a creature of unsuspected qualities, who will gladden and adorn our existence. . . . Let us consider the twofold decadence of the man who, on reaching a decisive turning-point in his life, is still disturbed by the need of emotions. He seeks and believes he finds these in the poisoned springs of a youth which degrades itself by the contact with senility and impels him towards his ruin. But here a new secret garden of woman is offered to him. He will behold the one whom he has never yet seen, beautiful with a new beauty, revealing the riches of an inner life."

As a matter of fact, a very large number of women begin, after the Change of Life, for the first time really to enjoy their sex spontaneously and happily. I even know a woman, aged 60, who *for the first time* at that age began to enjoy sex union. She was vital, charming and happy in it then and her husband's passion and delight in her increased after that age.

This woman is not at all abnormal; others are like her, although she was a little unfortunate in having to wait so long for the true realisation and enjoyment of the natural physiological process of sex union. There are many who, having enjoyed it but little in their youth and early middle age, after the freedom from anxiety of the menstrual period with its recurrent tendency somewhat to reduce the vitality, benefit when the natural vitality of the system tends to accumulate instead of waste, and they derive more spontaneous gaiety and real benefit from sex union than ever before. Women who have thoughtfully observed themselves and have had the confidence of others assure me that it is a usual thing both for sex desire and the capacity to give and to receive enjoyment from unions to be increased rather than diminished after the climacteric. It is impossible to say at what age this natural spontaneous benefit from and enjoyment in sex union comes to an end. It is recorded that an old lady when asked at the age of 80, at what time a woman ceased to enjoy union with her spouse replied: "You must ask someone older than I; I do not yet know."

Dr. Havelock Ellis, in his classical six-volumed work on the Psychology of Sex, says that there appear to have been but few systematic observations on the persistence of the sex impulse in women after the menopause. It is regarded as a fairly frequent phenomenon by Kisch, and also by Löwenfeld, and Bloom in America recorded a woman of 79, twenty years past the menopause, who said that both desire and gratification were as great or greater than before the menopause.

Dr. Maxwell Telling informs me that he agrees fully with this view, adding: "I have been researching on this point for many years, and I am quite satisfied as a result of direct enquiry. In any case the waning of desire is mostly very gradual, and the enjoyment even less so."

A case of my own raises this problem in another form. Mrs. A. stating: "I am a widow, with a grown-up family, and since losing my dear husband a few years ago I so often have acute sexual feelings and I wondered at my age (66) if it should be encouraged or repressed . . . or if you could prescribe anything to give me just a little satisfaction at such times as I do not care to discuss the subject with my own medical man."

The idea of an elderly woman enjoying sex life appears to some common minds as somewhat grotesque and revolting, because they think of it in terms of crude bodily action. But if Darby and Joan, having grown together all their lives, mingling the mental and spiritual needs still find delight and mutual enrichment in their unions, it is surely a thing of beauty.

The *duration* of the Change is another point about which people desire information. I have read much about the "Change" or Menopause, innumerable learned pronouncements as well as popular books and booklets addressed to women readers, and in none of them is there the direct, first-hand *evidence* of what *healthy*, *normal* women have felt and experienced which one desires to have. I cannot speak from personal experience, but I can give first-hand records of real cases which should be valuable. Some of the actual data given me in confidence in answer to a secret questionnaire I drew up are as follows:—

Mrs. A. B. "The disturbance of the Menopause began at 42, and was not quite over by 55. Sex desire was there all the time, and afterwards pleasure in union would have been as great or greater than before but for ignorance. Yes, spontaneous desire did arise at regular rhythmic periods afterwards, much as it did before. These phases of desire continued longer than before, when the period brought relief. Thought that it was wrong and unwise to enjoy sex union afterwards and so suffered greatly."

Mrs. A. F. "The disturbance of the Menopause began at 43 and lasted five years. Sex desire did not cease during that period. Afterwards, pleasure in sex union was probably greater. No, no rhythmic periods of desire could be detected. Desire was generally dormant but ready to be elicited and quick to respond. My husband had no idea that desire might return after the Menopause and expected it to cease altogether, and doubted whether it ought to be evoked or satisfied. Happy unions took place somewhat less frequently than formerly, perhaps once a week and occasionally more often, sometimes less. An even deeper joy and freedom in union was experienced than before, because one had no thought of consequences. Years of restraint, caution, withdrawal and so forth were superseded by absolute disregard of results. Hence the coitus was unimpeded and in consequence much more satisfying. There was the sensation of relief that nothing could happen which added to the pleasure."

A healthy, unmarried woman, Miss X.,

replied: "Disturbance of the Menopause between the ages of 49 and 54 when period ceased; disturbance lasted between two and three years longer. During the Menopause desire never left so far as recollection goes, and was certainly more active during the period of change, causing depression through repression and lack of understanding. Spontaneous desire was always dormant but spontaneously arising at intervals and more consciously so than before."

These random cases conflict with the "learned" pronouncement *ex-cathedra* of the gynæcologist who said: "It is customary to speak of the 'years' of the Change of Life, but why 'years' is not clear. . . . This process cannot take years; it is at most a matter of about ten months." (Dr. Bauer, *Women*, Engl. transl. 1926.) While this may often be true, it is certain that a lengthy "change" is also commonly experienced, as in the three typical cases, chosen at random, showing that each took a good many years to pass through the disturbances of the Menopause. Of more vital interest is the fact that all three cases testify to the continuance of sex desire all through and *after* the Menopause. Though I have a good deal of evidence about women who pass through a phase of revulsion towards sex life at this time, I think it is certainly true of the majority of normally healthy women that the capacity for, the enjoyment of and the benefit derived from sex unions after the Menopause are all maintained or increased. Were this universally understood, respected and utilised, how much added charm, stability and joy would life hold for maturing married couples! I know men who have been driven directly into the arms of prostitutes because of the *idea* that after the Menopause sex life with their own wives must finish. It is a commonplace among those who are best qualified to know that the institution of prostitution is very materially supported by married men whose wives are over 45. The repressed, disheartened, needlessly saddened lives of women with living husbands, who are deprived more acutely than are widows, must be counted in myriads through the ages. Why? Because of the false teaching of ignorant theologians which chanced to coincide with the disturbed attitude of mind of some miserable women during the Menopause. Verily the volume of the needless woe and ill-health in the world makes me weep for humanity. Who so deserving censure as he, whether teacher or priest, who has tampered with and barred the natural and spontaneous love-expressions between married lovers and thus sown seeds of misery in innumerable and unexpected places?

That the Change of Life in woman may take place at such an early date that a very large proportion of her married life is that continuing after the Change is seen by the fact that many women have had the Change by the age of 35. I rather fancy our grand-mothers, on the whole, had it earlier than people do to-day. The average age seems to be in the late forties and early fifties, and where a woman's vitality is very strong, her health good, and constitution sound, she may not anticipate it until the middle or late fifties. I think that the "late maturing type" I detected, and have described in *Radiant Motherhood*, has the Menopause later than other women. Two women of this type known to me were nearing 60 before the Change was completed. Whatever time the Change of Life comes, it has a few features which probably will be found to be almost universal, and which it may be of service, both to the husband and to the wife, to know.

I have often been consulted about one point, the liability to become unexpectedly pregnant after the Change has passed. It may be useful, therefore, to consider what are the outward phenomena connected with the Change of Life. The main physiological effect

N

(the only one which is apparent in a perfectly healthy, well-balanced woman) is that the monthly flow of menstruation gradually reduces itself and then perhaps for a few months becomes erratic, and finally ceases. I will leave it to the hectic books on the subject to describe the difficulties of this process such as hæmorrhage, etc., which some women experience. I am sure that there is no necessity for this if they are sufficiently intelligent to prevent anæmia and to take compensating compounds.

The period of disturbance of the "Change," however, is generally considered to be concluded and done with when the menstrual flow has entirely ceased; and when, say, for two or three months the menses have not put in an appearance, the woman generally considers the Change over. If, as is likely at this stage, she has for some time past decided that it was not in the interests of the child or of her existing family to have a late baby, she probably has been using some birth control or contraceptive method to prevent conception. When the monthly period ceases she stops this, and to her intense astonishment, perhaps a year, perhaps even after two years from the cessation of the menstrual flow, she finds herself pregnant. She is amazed, perhaps terrified, and thinks it "unnatural." Now the reason for the possibility of such pregnancy is that, the *ovaries* were still active, although the red coloured menstrual flow, which is the outward sign, and which is all that the majority of people reckon with in connection with a woman's rhythmic sex life, had ceased. This outward and visible sign is however only a subsidiary physiological feature correlated with but not an inherent part of the life of the ovaries, and it is in the ovaries themselves that the egg-cells are produced. The egg-cells, which come from alternate ovaries once each month, travel down to the womb and are fertilised on their outward way. These ova are minute colourless, invisible specks of jelly and are expelled from the ovaries and lost into the outer world without the knowledge of the woman at all.

It happens during most of the life of a woman the coloured menstrual flow is correlated with this process of the ovaries. Menstruation is an outward sign of what is going on, but it is not essential, and after the menstrual flow has entirely ceased, for a year or two (I am not sure but I think three years the maximum of extended fertility) the ovaries may continue to expel the colourless egg-cells which are fertilisable and which may establish an embryo and give rise to a perfectly successful baby. Therefore, I should advise every woman whose health or circumstances would make a late pregnancy a misfortune, to continue with any birth control method she has been using for a full three years after the Change of Life.

On the other hand, this affords a certain amount of hope and encouragement to those who passionately want a child, and who have never yet conceived. For instance Mrs. T., who married very late and was not very actively disturbed by sex life, was childless until just after the Change of Life, when she suddenly conceived the intensely desired baby. It almost appears as though there is a last spurt (one might call it) of potential fertility for a few months or a year or two just after the Change.

Then a word of advice to husbands is in place here. So many cases are known to me during the Change of Life or while it was incipient when the woman went through certain more or less natural reactions—reactions which I think would not manifest themselves had her sex life been entirely normal and perfectly happy, and had her health been perfect, but which, owing to the general imperfections of the current world do arise. Sometimes for a while (it may be a matter of a few months or it may be for

a year or more) the woman feels wearied by
sex, a little tired, overstrung, and not in the
mood to be approached. She may ask, as
I know Mrs. M. demanded of her husband,
that she should be "let alone" and that he
should expect no further married unions or
wifely "duty." Few reasonable men will
refuse such a request and force themselves
like bullies and tyrants on an unwilling wife,
and they make the best they can of it,
according to their type and circumstances.

Mr. M., I regret to say, was so strongly
sexed that he regularly employed prostitutes a
couple of times a week, but other men known
to me have felt themselves getting a little
older and the insistent need of sex experience
less strong. Then it was that they trained
themselves by one or other of the means of
self-control to do without sex union. But
thereafter comes the difficult time for the
wife. Some months, a year, two years or
later, when the Change of Life is accom-
plished, her balance restored, her vitality
and potentialities accumulating, she becomes
once more a normally sexed creature. Then
she is touchingly, even romantically eager to
resume the relation with her husband which
had been broken off at her own request.

The case of Mrs. Q. rises to my mind in
this connection. With all the finality that the

lonely mood generated by her physiological
state seemed to justify, she emphasised and
insisted to her husband that their sex life
was over. She claimed that they must in
future be merely the parents of their growing
family, and that for them union was for
ever concluded. The husband acquiesced:
but two years afterwards the wife came to
me in a state of acute despair, asking for
advice as to how she could possibly proceed
to get back her husband, to give him still
what was obviously required, and what she
herself was now only too eager to give
spontaneously and happily. Yet she felt too
shamefaced to confess and explain how
profoundly she had misunderstood herself
and the situation when she had made her
emphatic decree a couple of years before.
Fortunately by the simple expedient of being
entirely frank with her husband, supported by
my testimony that such a change of attitude
towards sex life and a restoration towards the
normal happiness is quite usual, the pair
entered upon a later phase of their lastingly
happy marriage.

My advice, therefore, to husbands whose
wives are entering upon, or passing through,
this period of Change is to realise that this
phase of temporary repugnance, sometimes
very emphatically expressed, may be ex-

perienced by their wives, and that, although they must not at the time endeavour to persuade them that they are wrong or to override their wishes, they should treat them with added consideration and apparent agreement so far as it is possible. Let them meet protestations of finality with a loving smile and "Let us wait and see," rather than an attempt to override their arguments at this time. This would be tactful and likely in the end to be successful. Then, after some months or a year or so, it is more than probable that the normal marriage relation may be not only successfully, but very happily resumed. It is important, therefore, that the husband in the meantime should not be disheartened, and not do what Mr. M. did and break up the married unity by going elsewhere. He should not for a moment consider that the true inner aspects of marriage had come to an end, and although he may have a temporarily difficult time, I think it is generally true of a worth-while man that difficulty does not daunt him when there is a reasonable chance of success in overcoming the difficulties, and in this connection I say emphatically there is.

Chapter XI

"The Change" in Men

THE title of this chapter may in itself be a surprise to the majority of readers, for remarkably little is known of the physiological phases occurring in men equivalent to the Climacteric or Change of Life in women. It is, of course, externally much less easy to recognise in men for in them it depends solely on internal reorganisation and there is no such characteristic and noticeable external feature as the cessation of the menstrual flow in women.

Many men are not conscious of any Change in themselves. That there is a climacteric Change of Life in a great many men, however, is certainly true, and this period has often given rise to a good deal of unhappiness and anxiety. Those who have told me of this phase in themselves, after having lived through it and come out on the other side successfully with added wisdom recognise that it was only fortunate chance which saved them, for no one was there to help with advice or knowledge. Generally men confide the facts which are then worrying them without in the least recognising their significance. Such men are astonished when told that they are only passing through the Climacteric, and that in a few months or a year or two all should settle down and things should be well with them again

Far too little is yet known about the subtleties of human sex life for anyone to be able to explain clearly just what is happening to men at this time. This chapter, indeed, must perforce be in the nature of a preliminary observation, a pointing out that here is a phenomenon worthy of attention.

The *obvious* outward sign of the Change in Women is the cessation of the menstrual flow: that this does *not* denote the cessation of her sex life is shown both by the fact that she may become pregnant and bear and nurse a child after the change, and that she continues to feel sex desire and to experience satisfaction in the orgasm after the change. At the time of the change an alteration of mental attitude towards sex is often apparent, but the phase is generally evanescent and a return to the normal is to be anticipated in favourable conditions.

To contrast what can be gleaned about

the man's "Change" with this: there is no
obvious outward cessation of any function,
but there is an inner involution of the sex
organs; this does not denote the cessation of
his sex life for the man can procreate children
after this and into an advanced age may both
feel sex desire and enjoy the satisfaction of
the orgasm. The most marked outward and
obvious sign of the Change in Men is a
mental one. So far as I can judge the mind
then tends to alter and this is most marked
in a man who has been very strongly sexed
and has even been licentious and indulged
in excesses in his youth. At the time of the
"Change" such a man may veer completely
round, and tends to condemn sex life, even
perhaps to abhor it. He may, after the Change
has passed, still feel sex desire and potency,
but he may then feel it to be a crime, a
lowering, a sin to be conquered. Such men
become the very bug-bears of youth and all
that is spontaneously healthy and happy in
natural sex life. They make fantastic claims
for "virtue," and uphold standards which, if
followed out, would put an end to human
life in a generation. They do not necessarily
cease to have sex connections themselves,
but often make these connections a source
of misery. After them such a man may weep
and wail and beat his breast crying *mea culpa*,

and thus involve his spouse in a sense of guilt over what should be a spontaneous happiness and a gift of nature to love.

A world-famous historical example of what I take to be such a mental reversal is seen in Count Leo Tolstoy. Tolstoy when a young man was intensely sexed, had relations with dozens of women, and then married. Thereafter he led an active sex life, gave his wife thirteen children (and some miscarriages), and expected his sex needs to be fulfilled all the time they were being reared. He had a powerful and enquiring brain, and a conscience very sensitive in its urgent desire to fulfil whatever at the time he felt to be his duty to God. When a lad and a young man he thought about sex, and considered what any logical mind must perceive after a few hours of thought, the different and conflicting ideals concerning it.

In the heyday of his maturity, the full tide of his bodily functioning, he adopted the ideal of an active sex life. Years passed: sex involution naturally took place, the Change came slowly, and by himself unperceived, upon him and then he "discovered" that all sex life was wrong, was the cause of all evil, and he denounced it in his writings and influenced the lives of those around him, upholding an ascetic standard of absolute "purity." *The Life of Tolstoy*, by Aylmer Maude, and Aylmer Maude's Preface to the Kreutzer Sonata accompanying his translation of the book, should be studied if this point interests my readers.

It is, I believe, not a mere coincidence that the ideas he had had and could have acted upon as a young man only took hold of him so as to be given active expression at and after the time of the Change. The Change left Tolstoy still well sexed and potent, and his desires were sufficiently strong to cause him to unite with his wife. But no longer was it in happiness and love, it was then a reproach. In conversation with Aylmer Maude, Tolstoy said one day when about the age of 70, "I was myself a husband last night; but that is no reason for abandoning the struggle: God may grant me not to be so again." Maude adds: "He was physically strong and active for years after that, and some of his greatest intellectual achievements still lay before him."

Something had altered the strong, prolific man so that he reverted to ideas which had tinged his boyhood and he took up the fantastic position of those who condemn all sex life as "lowering." Is it not of interest to observe the correlation between these mental phases and the physiological states? It is,

I believe, no mere coincidence that the ideas
he had and could have acted upon as a young
man had he then wished, only took hold of
him so as to be given active expression at and
after the time of the Change. May we not
perceive that the reversal of attitude is but
an outward expression of the internal alterations dependent on alterations of glandular
secretions?

The "reformed rake" is generally of an
age when the Change has set his mind in the
new direction. I think St. Augustine and
other early Christian Fathers did not reverse
their mental attitudes until the Change did
it for them. Yet, by their very powerful
personalities, and perhaps aided by the
extreme and impossible standards they set
in their later preachments, the Tolstoys and
St. Augustines of all sects and countries, have
impressed their later ideas on their fellows
and kept muddied and confused the human
currents of thought about life's most fundamental problems.

On a lesser scale, one sees the same
symptoms recurring in everyday men around
one. The sound wise old men are those whose
natures have, led by real love, maintained
after the Change normal and sweet communion with their mates.

Diverging from the type extremely exemplified by Tolstoy, is the other resultant of the physical alterations of the Change, and he is the man who becomes over-stimulated in sex interest at this time due to the enlargement of the prostatic gland. This is, of course, not a *necessary* or a direct result of the Climacteric, but it is one which is, in fact, very often correlated with the internal rearrangements arising when the grandular balance is disturbed. Mention has been made of prostatic enlargement in other connections (see p. 111, Chap. VII).

As in women, the date of the Change varies. Between fifty and sixty-five are the usual years. Probably on the average the years approaching sixty are the commonest time for this occurrence in men.

In an interesting Hunterian lecture (see *The Lancet*, 25th February, 1922, p. 297) Dr. K. M. Walker, when considering enlargement of the prostate, incidentally remarks: "It is true that active spermatogenesis may be seen in the seminiferous tubules of a nonagenarian and that the sexual life of the male has no abrupt termination. The menopause in his case is so gradual in its onset as to be almost imperceptible. Nevertheless a decline in sexual activity occurs and the genital tract of a man of 55 years shows unmistakable signs of involution."

Extremely little is available, however, in the scientific literature on the subject, and this chapter is written more from direct observation and confidences of sufferers than from summaries and collected observations published by others. Like those concerning impotence in a young man, and a general lack of sex vigour, the symptoms are such as cause the average man a certain amount of personal humiliation and vexation and he tends not to consult a man doctor—in fact not to consult anyone. He may perhaps speak of it to some friend or even a casual acquaintance, and then mention the symptoms in an indirect manner. Of the confidences brought to me spontaneously on this phase, the majority have been direct and verbal given only as opportunity arose—sometimes apparently by chance, as when meeting a man about some business affair, he may have begged the privilege of asking my opinion in view of my interest in rendering marriage happy for younger married people. I am often amazed at the urgency and the pathetic trust with which people seek for my advice.

A fairly typical example appears to be that of Mr. R. B., aged 58, very happily married and still very much in love with his wife, whom he obviously admires. He finds himself in the last few months quite unexpectedly incapable of maintaining the sex relation which has been established between them for many years. Although affection and the craving for union is present, sometimes even the power to unite, either the erection itself is very evanescent or the actual ejaculation and orgasm difficult to bring to completion. This is causing him intense humiliation and distress, all the more because his wife is misinterpreting it and thinking, as she has grown older with him, she is losing her physical attraction for him, that she is in some way to blame, and that she has been supplanted by a younger and fresher woman. She is mistaken and the man all the while truly protests that there is no other woman playing any part in his sex life, even in his thoughts and imagination. Although she may be an older woman to the rest of the world, to him she seems young as when they married and still has an intense attraction for him. His difficulty in making her understand this and believe it adds to his mental depression, for he is old-fashioned, romantic and very affectionate and would not hurt her feelings for the world. Yet much as he loves her, he simply cannot carry on with his "marital duties." At the same time he feels weary and depressed and in several other respects below par in a way that does not seem directly accounted for.

My cheering reassurance that he is simply experiencing the Change of Life was first an astonishment and then a relief. He brightened up immediately in the hope that it will be a phase through which he passes. Although after the phase of the Climacteric the sex potency does not return with such a degree of frequency or urgency as in a young man, sex potency does return, and is fully adequate to meet the needs of the loving and understanding wife who has grown old with him.

The capacity for union and the enjoyment and benefit from it may remain to a very advanced age. For older men, it seems also as though a method of union which I have always felt unwise for young men to practise may be adopted with benefit. That is what is called *coitus reservatus* by the Roman Catholics, who permit it, and also called *Karezza* by the American lady doctor who spread a knowledge of the method. Curiously enough, when called *Karezza* and thus mentioned in one of my books, the Roman Catholics in a recent legal action professed great horror and deep disgust towards the idea, while ignorant or pretending to be ignorant of the fact that this identical method

o

was very widely known, described and permitted as *coitus reservatus* by Roman Catholics in authority!

Anyone interested in this curious point should read what is said by the leading Roman Catholic authority, T. Slater, in *A Manual of Moral Theology*, 2 vols., and also the book *The Morality of Birth Control and Kindred Sex Subjects* (see Chapter VI), by a Priest of the Church of England.

The method briefly is that, after mutual passion has been roused and union effected, instead of leading up to an orgasm an attempt to reach complete calm, both mental and physical, should be made. This is achieved by the cessation of all physical movement and the centring of thought on the spiritual aspects of the beloved. In my opinion, an average, strong and unimaginative Englishman is not likely to achieve success in this type of union, but those in whom the vitality is not excessive undoubtedly may do so. I have heard from more than one woman that she and her husband have united in this way with not only a very soothing effect on the nerves, but with a great access of tender feeling.

This method was very closely approximated to by the Oneida Community and called by them "Male continence." A certain amount of instinctive prejudice has grown up against it on that account.

It is a method, in my opinion, in which the man is likely to gain more than the woman from the union. Whatever there may be against it, at any rate, it unites in deep affection the two who practise it. It is a method which may be well adapted for the later years of marriage; perhaps as an alternative to complete coitus with full ejaculation, which may take place at lengthening intervals, the method of *coitus reservatus* at intermediate intervals may be adopted so as to reduce the number of times that the man disburses seminal fluid. Several of the couples who have used *coitus reservatus* for many years tell me that there is no method of union which gives such a reaction of intense peace and loving comradeship, and such a sense of spiritual union as this.

A Lieutenant in the Army who himself has used it wrote of it in a letter to his medical man: "Advocacy of 'Karezza' is not the old asceticism in a new form. While being a delight physically, it is most absolutely satisfying psychologically, which is where all other methods break down. But it can never form a real satisfying consummation if one has any prejudice against it. One must give it a fair trial. It will appeal to thousands who would never be parties to the use of ordinary contraceptives."

The method seems to me only really suitable for aged or slightly abnormal people. Dr. W. F. Robie confirms this view from a wide medical experience and says: "The teachings of the Oneida Community and other sects that intercourse without emissions by either or both husband or wife may be postponed indefinitely to advantage are wrong. Occasionally, this is certainly a pleasurable and commendable love act, but if too frequently indulged in or to the exclusion of the complete natural act altogether it may render the man impotent and the woman neurotic. This has been proved to me repeatedly by couples who have tried it."

It is certainly unsuitable for the young, but possibly a knowledge of this method and the practise of it by older people may contribute to the happiness of the later years of marriage.

To assist the man to pass easily and successfully through his Climacteric, certain extracts of those glandular substances in which he is deficient or the balance of which is not being properly maintained, are very useful and should be recommended to every man who feels any such disturbance round about the age of sixty (see also Appendix A, No. 6).

Probably the most generally useful at this time would be a mixture of Lymphatic and Spermin. Some men may benefit more by Prostatic extracts or other specially suited to their individual needs.

Sometimes, greatly to his distress, a man becomes completely impotent for a few months or more at this time. After a few months or a year or two the disturbance should have passed, the balance of the whole system will have been adjusted to its lessened sex activity, and the man's general vitality and virility be re-established.

Those who have passed successfully through these difficult years are likely to live to a hale, hearty and happy old age. The neglect of these years, and particularly a neglect through a total misunderstanding of what is going on, has resulted in the generally recognised truth that round about the age of sixty is a dangerous time for men. If it were quite frankly and openly recognised and studied more in detail than it has been, I think much more could be done than has been done in the past to secure the successful passage of these few years. Its chief danger for men is the enlarged prostate with its consequences of urine retention, etc. I have just published a book on the subject which will, I hope, prove useful in preventing some of the worst troubles of this time; it is called *Change of Life in Men and Women.*

Some men think it derogatory or in the nature of a humiliation that they too should have a "Change of Life." That this should be so, is a reminiscence of a false attitude towards womanhood and her physiological characteristics. The truth is that men and women are, in many respects, much more like each other than the prime difference in their function in regard to child-bearing would lead us to suppose. I think it should make it easier for both of the married pair if they realised that they will both in a greater or less degree have some such disturbing period to pass through, based on similar causes with some of the same symptoms, and that this knowledge will help both to help each other through this time, when consideration and understanding are so essential.

Chapter XII

The Second Honeymoon:
the Human Duity

There's not the smallest orb which thou behold'st
But in his motion like an angel sings,
Still quiring to the young-eyed cherubins;
Such harmony is in immortal souls;
But, whilst the muddy vesture of decay
Doth grossly close it in, we cannot hear it.

W. SHAKESPEARE.

IF, as general experience proves to be practically best, the woman is a few years younger than the man, and if their marriage has been a long and happy and mutually successful one, it is quite likely that the Climacteric phases through which they pass may more or less coincide. If they are fortunate both may pass through the natural phases of involution with as little consciousness of trouble as a happy and healthy girl when entering womanhood. That is to say, with no disturbance or trouble at all. But even with the best will in the world this

cannot be achieved with certainty and some
ruffling of the surface may indicate the
deeper changes.

If this is so it may be an excellent plan
to travel quietly and easily, or to be away
from each other during the time that there
is a certain tendency for the union to be either
difficult or not particularly desirable. All
depends on individual circumstances and
how deeply they love each other in other
ways. For a couple whose main basis of
union has been the physical side of marriage,
probably a separation—a good long journey
with cheerful friends in opposite directions—
may be a very bracing and useful tonic.
Whether they go through the Change together
or at a distance from each other, if they
properly manage their lives the time will
come when the romantic love returns, leading
to a need of physical expression. Then let
them arrange a real honeymoon together.

So much has been written by all sorts of
"uplift" people on the advantage of a right
mental attitude that there is no need for me
to emphasise this point. I need do no more
than remind true wedded lovers that after
the Change of Life there should be a second
wooing, a second honeymoon, in which they
should find the rapturous beauty of a deep
peace and sense of unity, as well as the

expression of an enduring passion of mind as well as body.

Probably by this time their family will have grown up, or, at any rate, have reached the school or college age, and be sufficiently independent therefore to be left for a few months, and the two should have a real honeymoon jaunt, quiet, unhurried, doing things they really have wanted to do and perhaps have had to sacrifice for many years when the young children in the home were an hourly responsibility for the wife.

They should enjoy each other with a deeper understanding than when they had their first honeymoon. Then probably, if they were average people, each was rather self-centred and selfish. Now the multitudinous mutual interests and the exacting labours of rearing a family should have entered a phase of lessened responsibilities, leaving them time to embark together to explore realms of intellectual life and of potential creations. First let them take a well-earned spell of uninterrupted mutual joy, and plan out their future enterprises on their second honeymoon as they planned their lives together on their first. Frederick Harris said: "Marital partnership is a personal experience which is capable of yielding supreme satisfaction. To be associated with another person is the saltiest kind of fun. To be associated with the same person in a whole variety of vital enterprises is real living."

The second honeymoon would be for many women a time such as is needed to restore and sweeten again the personal love which had retracted and withdrawn to itself for the time being, disturbed by all the internal reorganisation that Father Time imposed. The second honeymoon may well be the sweetest time of the lives of a truly wedded pair.

Then should be renewed the physical nearness and dearness, the joy in each other with which the rearing of young children inevitably, to some degree, interferes. The second honeymoon should be as real a honeymoon as the first, and in it Dr. Robie's advice should be followed: "Kiss without shame, for she desires it, your wife's lips, tongue, neck; and, as Shakespeare says: 'If these founts be dry, stray lower where the pleasant fountains lie!'"

The experience of the bodily joys of the mutual life in the human duity is an enhancement of the time spent on earth. How can either of the deeply loving pair feel that there is any ageing of the other save in the outer casing of the body? If the spirit illuminates the life with its direct beam of consciousness in touch with the eternal, does it not glow through the body until one sees in a delightful old man or woman still the sparkling radiance of full power and capacity? The natural phases of the body waxing and waning escape the revolting features of the corruption of materialism, which is reflected in a dulled exterior or in disease and decay of mind and body.

As Jean Finot so wisely said (*Problems of the Sexes*, 1913): "Let us also educate love . . . to the higher comprehension of the entirety of life. Love will thus be greatly broadened because it will be spiritualised; it will be more solid and more lasting because it will have its roots in the soul and not in the beauty of the body which changes even more rapidly than the appetites of our senses. The axis of love will be shifted. . . . Physical joys will be doubled by the communion of feelings and of thoughts, and our life, grown richer and more intense in profound feelings and unknown joys, will become more dignified and more serene."

The body is both the garment and the instrument of the soul. Man's body, aching for the intoxication of the senses, finds that in it he has touched a deeper love, a serene and heavenly communion. The man who has not felt both aspects of love has not lived his life, or loved his wife, completely, nor can he feel either *in excelsis* without the other.

The deeply loving couple are to each other eternally young. Surely that must be so if the essential personality within each is an immortal spirit, dressed for a while in human flesh to carry on some good work in the world. Far too much stress has been laid in all sex matters on youth and the bodily externals of youth, and the love of the spirit has suffered so that bodily love has been less lovely and less lasting than it should be. All through life sex glands function and influence almost every cell in our bodies; and whether we attempt to deny it or not we are sexed organisms. We can do our best when we understand and encourage sex and do not thwart and deny it. Man and woman *in love* should lastingly enrich, not rend and torment and defraud each other.

Enduring passion not only builds the home upon a rock and places sharpened tools in the hands, peace in the mind and joy in the heart, it endows the spirit with wings to explore the empyrean accompanied instead of alone.

APPENDIX A

A Few Examples of Useful Prescriptions

APPENDIX A

A Few Examples of Useful Prescriptions

VARIOUS glandular extracts have been referred to in the text, and about their use. I should like to make a few further generalisations and emphasise the instructions given in the text. It is important to many people to know that these extracts are composed of chemical molecules and not actual cells, and that they are derived from animals used for food and properly and wholesomely slaughtered. The elaborate chemical molecules of which the extracts are composed are of specific benefit to the human system when the corresponding glands in the person may be deficient in activity. See also what is said on p. 45 and p. 47 in the text.

Some medical practitioners administer such glandular extracts by direct *injection* instead of by the mouth, but I do not at all advise injection for a great variety of reasons which would take one too far to discuss. But one simple reason may be readily grasped: We cannot by any human process exactly simulate the way these glandular extracts naturally enter the blood and lymph streams by infinitesimal amounts *continuously*. The best we can do is to take

several small doses a day, and to do this we can
without too great a strain on the memory, manage
say, to swallow a capsule three times daily, and
carry this on for several months. But can one
possibly ask or expect a busy medical practitioner
to give his time and attention to administer three
injections a day for months to an individual who is
approximately well any way, and only requires
better "balance" and "toning up"?

Emphasis should be laid on the warning that on no
account should anyone take more than the dosage
prescribed for them personally. For instance, if one
capsule daily is prescribed and is found to be of
benefit, he must *not* argue that two will double the
effect and hasten the cure: on the contrary, it will
probably only upset the balance in another direction. Take the advised amount and no more.

I think it may be useful to give a few examples
of useful prescriptions, indicating both the nature
of the extract and the kind of amounts which
compose an average dose per capsule. The number
of capsules to be taken daily, as well as the actual
detail of the prescription for each individual case,
should be settled for each person who proposes to
use these aids to health by his or her own medical
adviser.

A large number of makers market various forms
of extracts, and medical users of these products all
agree that they are very variable in their effect.
Some are sceptical about their efficacy as a result
of having employed unsatisfactory compounds.

Experienced medical users of the products have
found, and so far as I have been able to test them

personally, I may say my experience has been the same, that the *freshly prepared* extracts in gelatine coated capsules are the best. They are incomparably better than the dry compressed tablets so widely advertised.

The prescriptions referred to in the text were omitted in the first edition of this book at the expressed desire of a distinguished doctor of medicine who read the volume while it was in the press. Since its publication, however, I have had a very large number of protests both from lay and medical readers at the omission, and requests from a number of medical practitioners for these prescriptions. It has grieved me also that their omission has been misunderstood by some who have hitherto been my admirers, who have even been so disturbed as to suggest that I had been "nobbled" by the medical profession, and published this book in *their* interests! This is, of course, fantastical, as it was supposed to be in the best interests of the lay readers to omit the prescriptions.

In the time which has elapsed since the appearance of the first edition of the book all of the many expressed opinions have been in favour of the inclusion of the prescription, including even a spirited protest from Mr. Bernard Shaw, who said: "It was wicked of you to let your book go to press with that revoke about the prescriptions. You *must* reset the next edition, no matter what it costs." Not one individual of any sort or profession has supported the idea that they should be omitted. I am glad that my original intention can therefore

P

take effect, and they are now being included. Those who possess the first edition and care to write to my publisher will receive *gratis* separate reprints of pp. 211 to 212, which they can insert in their own volumes.

I wish to emphasize the importance of medical consultation wherever possible on the part of those desiring to utilize glandular extracts. The following actual case indicates why:

A reader of the first edition, a middle-aged woman, wrote to say she had been to many doctors for treatment for climacteric troubles, but had received no relief nor what she considered any expert treatment. She wrote privately to me asking me to send her personally my prescriptions. In the course of her letter she mentioned one or two points about herself which led me to suspect that it was not ordinary climacteric disturbance, but something more serious that was wrong with her. I gave her the name of a competent medical practitioner in her own district and urged her to seek his advice. He found that an immediate operation was necessary, and an enormous ovarian cyst was removed, the presence of which was the cause of the trouble. In such a case as this no amount of glandular extracts would have had any effect. By taking them she would have helped to create distrust in their use, because she would have said, "I took just what Dr. Stopes advised and it did me no good," and she would have risked her life for the want of the operation which was essential. This is an extreme case, but it serves to illustrate what I have said again and again throughout the preceding pages, namely, *consult your medical adviser*—if necessary, make him or her read this book; you will both be much better able to discuss your case afterwards.

1. Reference p. 48.

For sex-deprived women (see note, p. 212).

(*a*) Prostatic extract. 1½ grains per capsule.
(*b*) Prostatic extract. 1 grain ⎱ per capsule.
    Orchitic extract . 2 grains ⎰

2. Reference p. 73.

Lymphatic extract . 2 grains ⎫
Thyroid extract . ½ grain ⎬ per capsule,
Spermin extract . 2 grains ⎭

together with other extracts as indicated, and with or without glycero-phosphates (see note, p. 212).

3. Reference p. 105.

Orchitic extract . 1 or 2 grains ⎫
Thyroid extract . ½ grain ⎬ per capsule,
Pituitary (anterior) 1 or 2 grains ⎭

with or without other extracts as indicated (see note, . 212).

4. Reference p. 152.

Ovarian extract. . 3 grains ⎱ per capsule.
Thyroid extract . ½ grain ⎰

5. Reference p. 159

Ovarian extract . 2 grains ⎫
Mammary extract 1 or 2 grains ⎬ per capsule
Thyroid extract . ½ grain ⎭

6. Reference p. 196.

Suprarenal cortex	. 2 grains	⎫
Prostatic extract	. 2 grains	⎬ per capsule.
Spermin . .	. 1 grain	⎭

NOTE.—*All* the above are merely generalised prescriptions indicating approximately *average* dosage for the conditions described in the text, and should not be taken without further and particular consideration of each individual case.

The number of capsules of such dosage per day should vary from 1 to 3. The length of time the treatment is to be continued to show lasting results, approximately 2 to 3 months. Though an almost immediate benefit may sometimes (though by no means always) be felt, the treatment should be persisted in long enough to established the benefit, and the dosage gradually reduced to 1 capsule alternate days before ceasing use.

APPENDIX B

Bibliography of the Author's Sociological, Popular, and Scientific Works

APPENDIX B

Bibliography of the Author's Sociological, Popular, and Scientific Works

SOCIOLOGICAL WORKS

FOR GENERAL READERS

MARRIED LOVE. First published by Fifield, 1918, now in 24*th Edition*, published by Putnam & Co., Ltd. Pp. xxii, 1–170. Price 7s. 6d. net. *Translated into French, German, Spanish, Danish, Swedish, Dutch, Polish, Hungarian, Czech, Afrikaans, Portuguese.*

WISE PARENTHOOD. First published by Fifield, 1918, now in 23*rd Edition*, published by Putnam & Co., Ltd., 1918. Pp. xii, 1–62. Price 6s. net. *Translated into Danish, Swedish, German, Dutch, Czech, Spanish, Hungarian, Chinese, Portuguese, Afrikaans.*

A LETTER TO WORKING MOTHERS. Published by the Author, 1919, now by the Mothers' Clinic. Pp. 1–16. Price 3d. net.

RADIANT MOTHERHOOD. Published by Putnam & Co., Ltd., 1920, now in 8*th Edition*. Pp. ix, 1–236. Price 7s. 6d. net. *Translated into German, Spanish, Dutch, Hungarian, Portuguese, Czech.*

CONTRACEPTION—ITS THEORY, HISTORY, AND PRACTICE. First published by Bale, Sons & Danielsson, 1923. *Revised and Enlarged Edition*, with ten plates. Pp. xxvii, 487. Price 21s. net. Published by Putnam & Co., Ltd., 1931.

ENDURING PASSION. A continuation of MARRIED LOVE. First published by Putnam & Co., Ltd., 1928, now in 6th *Edition*. Pp. xvi, 1–220. Price 7s. 6d. net.

CHANGE OF LIFE IN MEN AND WOMEN. Published by Putnam & Co., Ltd., 1936, now in 2nd *Edition*. Pp. xiv, 1–294. Price 7s. 6d. net.

ROMAN CATHOLIC METHODS OF BIRTH CONTROL. Pp. xv. 235. Peter Davies, 1933. Price 7s. 6d. net.

PREVENTION OF VENEREAL DISEASE. Published by Putnam & Co., Ltd., 1921. Pp. vii, 1–52. Price 2s. 6d. net.

A NEW GOSPEL. Published by A. L. Humphreys, 1922, now by Hatchards. Pp. 1–27. Price 2s. 6d. net.

EARLY DAYS OF BIRTH CONTROL. Published by Putnam & Co., Ltd., 1922. Pp. 1–32. Price 9d. net. (Out of print.)

MOTHER, HOW WAS I BORN? Published by Putnam & Co., Ltd., 1923. Pp. 1–25. Price 9d. net.

THE CONTROL OF PARENTHOOD. By Bishop Russell-Wakefield and others. Edited by Rev. Sir James Marchant. 8th Impression. (One chapter by Dr. Stopes.) Published by Putnam & Co., Ltd., 1920.

QUEEN'S HALL MEETING ON C.B.C. Published by Putnam & Co., Ltd., 1921. Pp. 1–48. (Contains verbatim report of Dr. Stopes's speech.) Price 1s. net.

VERBATIM REPORT OF THE TOWN HALL MEETING. Published by the Voluntary Parenthood League, New York City, 1921. Pp. 1–23. (Contains verbatim report of Dr. Stopes's speech.)

THE FIRST FIVE THOUSAND. Being the First Report of the First British Birth Control Clinic. Published by Bale, Sons & Danielsson, 1925. Pp. 1–67. Price 2s. 6d. net.

BIRTH CONTROL TO-DAY. First published by Bale, Son & Danielsson, now published by Wm. Heinemann Ltd., 1934. Pp. 237. Price 3s. net.

THE HUMAN BODY AND ITS FUNCTIONS. Published by Gill, 1926. Pp. 221, 53 text figs. Pls. I–VII. Price 6s. 6d. net. *Cheap Edition*. Putnam & Co., Ltd., 1929. Price 6s. net.

SEX AND THE YOUNG. Published by Gill, 1926. Pp. 190. Price 6s. 6d. net. *Cheap Edition*. Putnam & Co., Ltd., 1929. Price 4s. 6d. net.

MOTHER ENGLAND, a Contemporary History, self-written by those who have had no historian. Published by Bale & Danielsson, 1929. Pp. viii, 206. Price 10s. 6d.

PRELIMINARY NOTES on the analysed data of Ten Thousand Cases attending the Pioneer Mothers' Clinic. Published by the Clinic. Pp. 44. Price 6d.

YOUR BABY'S FIRST YEAR. Published by Putnam & Co., Ltd, 1939. Pp. xii, 284. Price 7s. 6d. net.

ELEMENTARY SCIENCE

ANCIENT PLANTS. Published by Blackie & Son, 1910. Pp. viii, 1–199. Price 4s. 6d. net.

THE STUDY OF PLANT LIFE. Published by Blackie & Son, 1906. Pp. xii, 1–202. Price 3s. 6d. net.

Exploitation of Plants. Edited by Professor Oliver. Published by Dent. (One chapter in this.)

Sportophyte, the Botanical Punch. Founded and Edited for the years 1911–1914.

PLAYS

Plays of Old Japan, The Nō. (With Prof. J. Sakurai.) Published by Heinemann, 1913. Pp. 1–102 illustrated. Price 5s. net. (Out of print.) Facsimile edition, paper covers. Eclipse Press. Price 3s. 6d. net.

A Japanese Mediæval Drama. Transactions of the Royal Society of Literature, vol. 29 (separate), pp. 1–26. (Out of print.)

Conquest. A Three Act Play. Published by French. Pp. 1–94. Price 1s. net.

Gold in the Wood and the Race. Two Plays published by Fifield, 1918. Pp. 1–101. Price 2s. net.

Our Ostriches. Produced at the Court Theatre. Published by Putnam & Co., Ltd., 1923. Pp. 1–105. Price 2s. net.

A Banned Play and a Preface on the Censorship. Published by Bale, Sons & Danielsson, 1926. Pp. 1–144. Price 5s. net.

LITERARY AND TRAVEL

Love Songs for Young Lovers. Heinemann, 1939. Price 5s. net.

Oriri. Poem. Heinemann. Price 3s. 6d. net.

Man, other Poems and a Preface. Published by Heinemann, 1914. Pp. 1–76. Price 3s. 6d. net.

A JOURNAL FROM JAPAN. Published by Blackie, 1910. Pp. 1–250. Price 7s. 6d. net. (Out of print.)

Also fairy stories in the *Fortnightly Review*, *English Review ;* articles in *The Times*, *Manchester Guardian*, *Science Progress;* reviews in the *Athenæum*, etc.

SCIENTIFIC MEMOIRS, *Etc.*, EMBODYING NEW DISCOVERIES

FOR SCIENTIFIC EXPERTS

THE SPONTANEOUS COMBUSTION OF COAL. (With Prof. R. V. Wheeler.) Bulletin No. 1 of "Fuel." Published *Colliery Guardian*, London, 1923. Pp. 1–125, 2 plates and text figs. Price 5s. net.

THE CONSTITUTION OF COAL. (With Dr. R. V. Wheeler.) Monograph, published by H.M. Stationery Office for the Department of Scientific and Industrial Research, 1928. Pp. 1–58, plates i–iii. Reprinted. Price 2s. net.

THE CRETACEOUS FLORA IN THE BRITISH MUSEUM (NATURAL HISTORY), PART II: LOWER GREENSAND (APTIAN) PLANTS OF BRITAIN. Published by the Trustees of the British Museum, 1915. Pp. i–xxxvi, 1–360, plates i–xxxii, 112 text figs. Price £1 1s. net.

THE 'FERNLEDGES' CARBONIFEROUS FLORA OF ST. JOHN, NEW BRUNSWICK. Published by the Geo-

logical Survey of Canada: Memoir 41, Ottawa,
1914. Pp. i–vi, 1–142, plates i–xxv, 21 text figs.
Price 7s. net.

THE CRETACEOUS FLORA IN THE BRITISH MUSEUM
(NATURAL HISTORY), PART I: BIBLIOGRAPHY,
ALGÆ AND FUNGI. Published by the Trustees of
the British Museum, 1913. Pp. i–xxiii, 1–285,
plates i–xi, 25 text figs. Price 15s. net.

Also a large number of memoirs published by
learned societies, the Phil. Transactions of the Royal
Society, scientific Annals etc.

Printed in Great Britain by
UNWIN BROTHERS LIMITED, LONDON AND WOKING

Reviews and Opinions

MARRIED LOVE

From an Article referring to *Married Love*, in *The Medical Review of Reviews*, Vol. 25, No. 2, February 1919, by DR. HAVELOCK ELLIS: "This seems to represent the most notable advance made during recent years in the knowledge of women's psycho-physiological life."

PROFESSOR G. STANLEY HALL, in his book *Morale* (Appleton, 1920, p. 266), says of *Married Love*: "Dr. Stopes has spoken the boldest, truest, and sanest word so far accessible in print which all, not only the newly wed, but those about to wed, perhaps especially husbands, should read and ponder."

"Dr. Marie Stopes has endeavoured to meet the need of healthy young people of the educated class for information as to the sexual responsibilities of marriage. Though not a medical woman, the author has special qualifications for this task; with high scientific attainments she combines literary skill, sympathetic insight, idealism, and more than common courage. . . . To the married and to those about to marry, provided they are normal in mind and body and not afraid of facing facts, this should prove a most helpful book."— *British Medical Journal*.

"This book considers its subject almost entirely in its physiological and medical aspects, though Dr. Stopes has something to say, too, on the spiritual side of the bearing towards each other of husband and wife. . . .

MARRIED LOVE—contd.

Much of what she has to say is calculated to prevent impaired health, misunderstanding, and unhappiness."
—*Times Literary Supplement*.

"This is a remarkable book which gives much information regarding the physiology of marital life. . . . All medical men and medical women should read and study this book. They cannot fail to glean from its pages valuable information."—*Medical Times*.

"Like all Dr. Stopes's writing, it is clear, thoughtful, penetrating, and undoubtedly is a scientific contribution towards a subject which a decade ago would have been taboo. . . . Our advice is for women to read it and for men to read it, for there is here stated a real problem which is specifically English."—*English Review*.

The following endorsement was drawn up to meet official objection in America: " We consider the book *Married Love*, by Dr. MARIE C. STOPES, to be a valuable contribution to the Sex Education Movement now being conducted in all civilised countries of the world. We approve of its publication and general circulation."—
(*Signed*) Arnold Bennett, Havelock Ellis, W. R. Inge (Dean of St. Paul's), W. Arbuthnot Lane, W. J. Locke, Aylmer Maude, E. Phillips Oppenheim, G. Archdall Reid, G. Bernard Shaw, May Sinclair, H. G. Wells, M. Stanley Wrench, Eden Phillpotts, Leonard Merrick, A. E. W. Mason.

CONTRACEPTION—ITS THEORY, HISTORY, AND PRACTICE

"From a medical point of view there can be little doubt that there are cases in which the prevention of child-bearing in married women is called for, and in which it would be difficult and indeed undesirable to attain this object without the use of one of the methods here described. The simplicity of that advised by Dr. Stopes and its probable efficiency commend its adoption when medical opinion is in favour of the avoidance of pregnancy. If, as Dr. Stopes believes, the adoption of such a method would prevent the frequent production of abortion, very considerable benefit would ensue to the health of women. . . . There can be no doubt as to her sincerity of purpose and the labour involved in the compilation of the book. It contains much information not procurable in any other volume, and may be recommended for perusal by members of the medical profession."—*Medical Journal of Australia*.

"Dr. Stopes sets out with precision and no little literacy grace the problem of contraception. . . . Much of the evidence contained in the book is quite unobtainable elsewhere."—*Lancet*.

"The book is valuable and should be read by all interested in racial welfare."—*Medical Review*.

"Some such book as this had to be written, and this is very well written."—SIR ARCHDALL REID in *Nature*.

Q

CONTRACEPTION—ITS THEORY, HISTORY, AND PRACTICE—contd.

"This problem will undoubtedly occupy a more prominent position in the future, and to those who wish to study it we can recommend this volume."—*Journal of State Medicine*.

"This highly important question cannot be studied completely and dispassionately without reference to her distinctly remarkable book."—*The Hospital and Health Review*.

"The book is unique and marks a new era in literature germane to this subject."—*Medical Times*.

"Nurses and midwives who work among the poor should be able to give advice upon this topic when called upon to do so, and for this purpose they will find Dr. Stopes's work invaluable."—*Nursing Mirror*.

"The book is supremely important, and its author is one of the most important women of our time, for almost single-handed, she is fighting a crusade which successful or the reverse, cannot fail to have a momentous effect on our civilisation."—*Scottish Nation*.

"This book will meet with opposition only from those who desire to suppress the facts."—PROF. CARR-SAUNDERS in *The Nation and Athenæum*.

WISE PARENTHOOD

"Its subject is birth control, and it gives in the plainest possible language information as to the ways—or way—in which control can be practised, with the least possible detriment to health, morals, and æsthetics. . . . If medical men and women will not put at the disposal of the general public such knowledge (in any case it is by no means exhaustive) as they possess on this subject, it was inevitable that someone should do what they have left undone; and we may be thankful that the person who has done, or begun to do this, should be Dr. Marie Stopes."—*The Common Cause*, December 27, 1919.

"I would strongly recommend any who are interested in the practical aspect [the scientific method of birth control] to read a little book which has just appeared from the pen of Dr. Marie C. Stopes, *Wise Parenthood*." —C. KILLICK MILLARD (Medical Officer of Health for Leicester), in *Medical Officer*, December 7, 1918.

"The method is that which people, including many doctors, want to know. . . . It meets the immense æsthetic difficulties. . . . The work is especially for those happy people who recognise the kindred duty and delight of having, by a healthy mother, healthy children. The wretches who wish to avoid all children are punished as only great offenders are punished, by the fulfilment of their desire. This little book, however, may show them the risks which they are incurring."— *The Hospital*.

"The author ably presents the case for birth control from the scientific point of view. She criticises several of the more important birth-control methods at present employed, and she gives a detailed description of a method which she considers reliable and safe. . . . No medical man or medical woman should fail to secure a copy and read it carefully."—*Medical Times*, December 1918.

RADIANT MOTHERHOOD

"Luminous with that sense of dignity which Dr. Stopes brings to matters which were shameful secrets to our forefathers. An intelligent study of Dr. Stopes's works (and a practical application of their teachings) would see the human race transformed in a few decades. Where else is there a hope for a sick and weary world but in the nurseries? 'A book for those creating the future,' says Dr. Stopes—a true word."—*Daily Express*, August 1920.

"For masses of women, to whom sex, as the result of Puritanism, is a sealed book, who are expecting to be mothers, and no less to youthful husbands, this disquisition on the fruits of wedlock should be really useful. . . . Dr. Stopes is doing for women a Trojan work." —*English Review*.

"Dr. Stopes's new book will have as many admirers as her former works have had. . . . To be sure there will be critics, for her teaching is too challenging to pass unheeded. At least her critics must admit that Dr. Stopes has a high ideal of motherhood and a real literary gift "—*Lancet*, October 30, 1920.

"The perfect frankness with which Dr. Marie Stopes deals with the great questions of love and parentage . . . is the way of true illumination."—*Pall Mall Gazette*, August 1920.

"A valuable, simple, and safe guide through the perplexities that are in store for most married people, and which, without instruction, they generally have to solve in some way by groping and often at the cost of unhappiness. . . . The book is addressed in reality nearly as largely to husbands as to wives, and its chapters will in many cases provoke the gratitude of both by explaining them to each other."—*Manchester Guardian*, October 5, 1920.

ENDURING PASSION

GEORGE BERNARD SHAW says: "Life, especially married life, is unnecessarily troubled and occasionally wrecked because we have no technique of marriage; and this ignorance is produced by the deliberate suppression of all responsible information on the subject. England has an expert instructress in the person of Dr. Marie Stopes; . . . numbers of needlessly unhappy marriages have been set right by her instruction."

"We dare wager that of the many married people who will read this book, the great majority will rise up and call its author blessed. . . . She is both the first person and the only person who has shouted from the house-tops with an effective carrying voice, the message that there is such a thing as a *technique* of married life which demands and repays consideration, study, and experiment. And she is perhaps both the first and the only person who has vividly realised the immense amount of human happiness which runs to waste, the immense volume of physical and spiritual maladjustment which is generated by the failure of married couples to master the technique which in varying degrees governs their physico-spiritual relationship."—*The Woman's Leader*.

"The world owes a debt to Dr. Marie Stopes."—*Plebs*.

". . . a praiseworthy effort to assist men and women to the maintaining and, where it does not exist, to the establishing of a state of sexual equality."—BOWEN PARTINGTON in *Health and Strength*.

"Worthy of careful study."—*The New Leader*.

"Clear, straightforward and wholesome."—*Daily Herald*.

DR. MARIE STOPES'S LATEST BOOK

CHANGE OF LIFE IN MEN AND WOMEN

"This is a useful book for middle-aged men and women, as well as for the younger people who the author is anxious should read it and avoid some of the pitfalls that wrong methods of living will bring about in the forties. Dr. Stopes deals with the change of life in women very sensibly, showing how it need not necessarily be a time of illness; she is insistent that this change does not necessarily mean the cessation of child-bearing and that it certainly does not mean the death of sexual desire.

"But the important part of the book from the author's point of view is the chapters which deal with the change of life in men, a subject which she tells us medical men have always neglected. An understanding of this climacteric would help married people to be more tolerant of each other when sexual maladjustments occur in middle life, and the early diagnosis of prostate trouble would save many men from major operation later on."—*Times Literary Supplement*.

". . . this is a most useful book. It draws attention to a most important problem which is all too frequently neglected, either through apathy, or more often because the matter is supposed to be indelicate. Specially interesting and important are the information and advice which are given regarding the male change of life, for the problems of the male are almost entirely neglected by other writers. Of course, the corresponding period in a woman's life is treated with equal detail. This book will provide an answer to most of those sexual and hygienic problems which arise at the climacteric, and it should do so much to rob this transitional period of its imaginary terrors."—*Aberdeen Press and Journal*.

MAUDE ROYDEN, D.D., C.H., writes to the author: "I can never tell you how grateful I am to you for writing this book."